ABOUT THE BOOK

The graceful gazelle galloped alongside his friend, the giraffe. Endomy had just finished giving himself a dust bath, and Reza, the colobus monkey, crooned his "Roo-roo-roo" as he danced on the mountainside of Kilimanjaro. Once again Walter Wilwerding brings you Africa, through tales and pictures of wild beasts, large and small.

"The Big One" is the title story and is about Endomy, a forty-year-old bull elephant. Wanting to make a huge profit on his ivory tusks, African poachers choose Endomy as their victim. Endomy escapes but the law of the hunter and hunted prevails. All of the stories portray this theme, the crisis faced by every animal that is the prey of others.

W.J.Wilwerding

THE BIG ONE

AND OTHER BEASTS • BY

WALTER J. WILWERDING

illustrated by the author

G. P. PUTNAM'S SONS

New York

FOREWORD

Again I am presenting a number of tales about African beasts, large and small. Once more, I have lived with them in memory. People often ask me how I obtained my material for these stories. It is really rather elementary. I lived among them and watched them every day to see how they lived and what they lived on. It was not always pleasant to see what some of them lived on, for they ate others. However, many of them lived relatively peaceful lives, except that they were ever watchful not to be eaten by predators.

It was possible to study the ways of these creatures very closely, as they spent their lives in a rather limited territory that they knew as their home. I could be pretty sure that if I went to a certain place at a certain time, I would find the animals I was seeking. Some of the small ones stayed within the rather narrow confines of a territory they regarded as home. It was thus with the mongooses that lived in deserted termite mounds quite close to where I stayed in an African hut near Lake Basotu, in Tanganyika. Daily, I watched the mongooses at their hunting, hearing them murmur like people, as they searched the grass for grasshoppers.

Hoofed veld animals were everywhere and easy to study. It was not difficult to watch the elephants from up close. One could walk very near to these big beasts while they were drinking, feeding or dusting themselves. It was just a matter of watching the wind direction. A friend once said to me, "I believe that one could walk right up to an elephant and grab him by the tail." I am sure that he was right, but one wonders what one would do when one let go of the tail.

I shall always remember the little gazelle and his friend, the big giraffe. I often saw them touch noses. And I will never forget Old Wildy, the bull gnu. He was very old when I knew him and I was young, for this was on my first safari, in 1929. Africa was new to me then and a very high adventure. On later safaris, to keep this fresh

5

feeling of adventure, I kept moving to new parts that I had not visited before. Thus, I covered quite a considerable part of Tanganyika, Kenya, Uganda, and the Congo. I was everlastingly drawing, painting, photographing, and taking notes of the animals and the land they occupied.

I came away from each safari with portfolios bursting with pictures and notes. These, within the limitations of the pages there are in a book, I am trying to share with the reader. I hope that I have been successful in bringing Africa to you, as it was when I saw it and heard its calls of birds and beasts, and as I smelled its blossom-scented air in the dew-covered African morning. If type and pictures can succeed in this, then, here is Africa for your enjoyment.

Two stories that appear in this book: "The Big One" and "Tiny of the Thornbush" (which first appeared as "The Little One"), were first presented in *Boys' Life* magazine in 1957 and 1959. Three of the other stories first appeared in *Blue Book* magazine about twenty-five years ago and have been rewritten for this book. All the other stories appear here for the first time. The illustrations are all new, having been made especially for this book from sketches and studies that I made directly from the animals and landscapes in Africa.

WALTER J. WILWERDING

CONTENTS

1: The Big One

In the midst of the dry, yellow grassland — ringed by the everlastingly blue hills of Uganda; with flat-topped thorn acacias and cactuslike candelabra-euphorbia trees scattered in every direction — there was a low, green spot from which, now and then, little cattle egrets rose with a flutter of white wings. Any wild beast of the veld, even without his keen scenting powers to guide him, knew that the lush green vegetation and flocks of white heron meant water. It was the only water hole left in the veld and bush country between Lake Edward and Lake George, for the dry season had lingered overlong and the rains were much overdue.

The big, gray, heavily tusked elephant bull did not worry about the

9

dwindling water hole. He could readily walk to either big lake for a drink and bath, or to the riverlike channel that connected the lakes. But in the heat of afternoon, he sometimes drank at the small water hole. Then, with blasts from his trunk as from a fire hose, he squirted himself with the muddy water. Having had his drink and bath, he scraped up dirt and threw this over his back. Apparently the bath was only for cooling purposes.

Afterward, he would go to a thicket of thornbushes and trees. Walking inside, he stood beneath the flat-topped green canopy of an umbrella-mimosa tree, resting his long tusks in a crotch to relieve himself of their great weight.

With his thick wrinkled skin caked with drying mud, he looked like a huge gray shadow in the dappled sunlight filtering through the leaves. Eleven feet high he stood on his pillarlike legs.

"*Endoomy*," the Uganda tribesmen called him. In their language, this meant a really big, old, smart he-elephant with great ivory tusks. He was all of these things, about forty years old and in the prime of his life and powers — wise from his experiences with men and beasts in the African wilds.

Endoomy's long, stout, curving tusks, polished near the tips from much digging at tree roots, weighed together well over three hundred pounds. The right tusk was a bit shorter than the left. Like most elephants, he was right-tusked as we are right-handed. Since the right tusk was used so much for digging, it was worn more than the left. It was only because of his wisdom and endurance that he had thus far saved both his tusks and his life from hunters who coveted his ivory treasure.

Endoomy had learned from the many painful wounds he had received from hunters that it was best to run fast and far when he scented these men. Since he could not shoot back at them, he was wise enough to run away and avoid them. Thus he had survived.

He should not have been obliged to worry about ivory hunters. This place he had come to was a protected reserve for animals, and no hunting was allowed here. He did not know this. He only knew that here hunters did not molest him and his herd. No longer was it necessary to go to drink at night and be ever alert by day. Gradually, the old fears about hunters left him.

Now he and his herd went to drink at high noon on the shores of

Lake Edward and Lake George and on the Kazinga Channel connecting these two lakes. This had always been the habit of the elephants before hunters had molested them, and they now reverted to their age-old habits.

The African people who lived in the grass-thatched and mud-plastered huts near the lake were fishermen. Endoomy learned to know them by sight. While he and his herd drank and bathed, with pelicans, cormorants, and hippopotamuses as company, the African fishermen were out in their dugout canoes. They arranged set lines on long poles stuck in the mud and put out nets. The fishermen attended to their business and the elephants minded theirs.

Samaki, an African fisherman of about twenty — big, muscular, with closely cropped hair — sat in his narrow, dugout canoe gathering catfish from his set lines. He wore tattered khaki shorts and was barefooted; his even white teeth showed in a satisfied smile as he pulled in catfish weighing seven and eight pounds each. Then his dark face suddenly sobered at the thought that he got a half shilling each for the fish, regardless of weight. The Punjabi fish dealers who came to haul the fish away in trucks paid for the fish by the piece instead of by weight. Samaki thought about this while keeping a wary eye on the hippopotamuses that could come to the surface under a dugout canoe and upset it.

As Samaki pulled in his fish, he looked across the water to where some elephants had come to drink on the shore. Though this was an everyday sight to him, he took a good look at the big bull elephant that was drinking with the herd. Samaki saw that this bull had unusually heavy ivory tusks. He knew that one did not sell ivory by the tusk, but by the pound. The ivory on this elephant bull would bring as many shillings as he would get for twelve thousand pounds of fish.

After Samaki had paddled his canoe to shore, he could still see the elephants at their drinking. He watched them until they walked away into the trees. All the way back to his village, he thought about the big bull's ivory.

It was dark when the Africans sat about their evening meal of corn-flour mush, fish, and bananas. Samaki conversed in low tones with Emzay, a withered old African who lived in the hut next to his. Emzay's hair was gray, as was his thin, pointed beard. He was wrapped in an old blanket, trying to keep his thin frame warm. Scraggly teeth held an old pipe made from a small gourd and a hollow reed stem. The old fellow had been a mighty hunter in his youth. The ways of the wild and the beasts that inhabited it were as plain to him as the palm of your hand. Often he told tales of hunting elephants and hippopotamuses. He had hunted in the days of the spear and bow and arrow. One had to be a very good tracker and hunter to bring down big game with these weapons.

Samaki told Emzay about the big elephant bull with the long, heavy ivory tusks. "He is an endoomy. Never have I seen one like him come to drink at this lake. Perhaps he came from the big forest."

Thinking this over for a time, while he thoughtfully sucked at his homemade pipe, Emzay answered, "Yes, the pools in the big forest are dry now; the elephants come out to the water of the lake."

"Such a big endoomy," mused Samaki. "His ivory would bring many shillings."

Emzay's bloodshot old eyes lit with a light rekindled by youthful memories of the hunt. Speculatively, he looked at the young man and said nothing.

"It would be easy to shoot this big fellow," continued Samaki. "These elephants pay little attention to us fishermen."

"What would you shoot him with?" inquired Emzay. "And once you shot him, what would you do with his big body and with his ivory? The tall white bwana on the hill would not like that. You would end up in jail instead of getting rich on ivory."

"One could shoot him back in the bush country," returned Samaki, "and one could hide the ivory in the bush in another place. I know a man who will buy the ivory. You know much about elephant hunting Emzay. We could get rich."

For a moment the light rekindled in the tired old eyes, but then the spark faded as Emzay answered with a sigh, "I am too old; the hunting days of my youth are far away. One could not use a musket. It would make too much noise. This would be work for a poisoned arrow — silent and deadly. I am no longer the young hunter who can sneak up close to an elephant and pull the stout bow." Reaching for a hot coal from the fire, he relit his pipe.

Samaki sat for a time saying nothing. Then, rising to his feet, he remarked, "I must get some sleep. Tomorrow I have nets to attend and also some other business to see to. We will talk about this again tomorrow. Good night."

Out in the velvety black of the African night, a lion roared and hippopotamuses bellowed. In an acacia thicket, a big bull elephant stood with his family herd and was entirely unaware that men plotted to take his life.

By the fire again the next evening, Samaki and Emzay sat smoking their pipes. Reaching forth with a stick to stir the coals of the fire, Samaki remarked, "I saw the endoomy again today. I was close with my canoe and got a very good look at his tusks. Those tusks will buy many things."

"Ivory in an elephant's mouth buys nothing," answered Emzay.

Samaki laughed and said, "Then we will take the ivory out of his mouth."

"How do you propose to do it?"

"Shoot the endoomy, how else?"

"And what will you shoot him with?"

"The poisoned arrow that you spoke about."

It was Emzay's turn to laugh. "You could not hit the side of a mountain with an arrow, Samaki. All your life you have been a fisherman. One does not catch elephants with hooks and fishing nets."

Testily, Samaki answered, "I have a friend who shoots birds and small animals with arrows. I have arranged for him to do the shooting. You will make the poison for the arrows."

"Now we are three," mused Emzay. "The ivory fortune dwindles with partition."

"There will be enough for all," answered Samaki. "I will now go to see my friend. I have also talked to the Punjabi who buys ivory. He is the one who buys my fish. No one will think of looking for ivory tusks in a fish truck. For your third of the profit, you will make the arrow poison. Your part is easy."

Emzay smiled and shrugged his shoulders. Samaki went to visit his friend at another hut.

The next night, Samaki brought his friend Winda to see Emzay. Winda, dressed in shorts and faded jersey, was a medium-sized, slightly built young man, wearing the close-cropped hair of African young men. He was perhaps a year younger than Samaki, good-looking and rather quiet by nature. Winda sat silent for a time and then he said, "I have been thinking about this and I think that I will not shoot this elephant."

Impatiently, Samaki threw a stick at the fire. "Why not?" he exploded.

"Because I do not wish to share a place in jail with you Samaki. The big white bwana on the hill does not want people to shoot his elephants."

"Whose elephants?" jeered Samaki. "They are as much ours. You shoot birds and small animals with your arrows. The bwana also would not like this if he heard about it."

Dismayed at this turn in the conversation, Winda answered, "The bwana does not care about the small things that I shoot for the pot. He does not want the big animals killed."

"The bwana says that no one may kill anything here," retorted Samaki. "This is one of those places where animals are to live without being hunted. Do not ask me why; it is one of the white man's follies. If someone told him about your hunting, you would have a place in his jail. Think it over. There will be no added risk in shooting the elephant."

So, after more persuasion and a few more veiled threats of exposure, Winda finally agreed to join the hunt. However, he agreed to do only the shooting. Samaki was to be the one who would chop out the ivory tusks, hide them and dispose of them later. Old Emzay, for his part, was to brew the poison for the arrow tips. And so the first act of the plot to kill Endoomy was staged.

The following night, while others slept, old Emzay was occupied with something that he had not done for many years. That day, he had gathered leaves and branches of a certain small tree. These he now boiled for a number of hours. He then strained out the leaves and bark and continued to boil the poisoned liquid until it was thick and looked much like pitch. This substance he carefully placed on a sheet of bark. He then rubbed his hands and body with the fleshy and juicy leaves of a kind of sage. This was done to remove any of the poison with which he may have come in contact.

This poison was exceedingly potent and would quickly kill any animal shot with a poisoned arrow. Emzay smeared some of this poison on arrow tips that he had sharpened to a razor edge. Now he carefully wrapped each arrow tip in a thin piece of animal skin. Again, he very carefully rubbed his hands with the juicy leaves to rid himself of any trace of poison. The second act of the plot to kill Endoomy was finished.

The burden of the plot fell upon the shoulders of Samaki. This sullen young man planned to hide the bow and poisoned arrows in his dugout canoe, among the poles that he stuck in the mud with lines and baited hooks for catfish. Who would look to see if some of the poles were shorter? After he had put out his set lines, he would go ashore and hide his canoe in the papyrus somewhere along the Kazinga Channel. Later, when the time was ripe, he would walk empty-handed to the canoe and sneak out the bow and arrows. He would then take to cover so he could go unseen through bushes to the place where he expected to hunt the big elephant.

Samaki knew about the low green place in the veld where there was water. He had seen the elephants going toward this place. It was the only logical place in which to wait for the big bull. Any hunting of the elephant when he came to the big lake to drink would be too much out in the open. All the fishermen would see it and the news would spread quickly. This hunting would have to be done in a secretive manner.

Things worked well for Samaki. No one saw him hide his canoe in the papyrus. No one saw him later when he went to get the bow and arrows. He wended his way by a devious route through the thickets of bushes and trees until he was at the small water hole. Looking about to see that no game guards were about, he hid the bow and arrows in a dense thicket near the water hole. He had worried about the African game guards, especially one named Lakana, who was the sergeant of the guards. These uniformed guards of the game warden's were always on the alert for poachers, for this was in a national park where no animals were allowed to be molested. One never knew when the guards would show up or where they would be next.

This night, Samaki sought Winda to tell him that the place for the hunt had been selected and that the poisoned arrows were hidden near the spot. The next day they would try their luck. Winda had little stomach for this business, but Samaki assured him that he could go on his way after the shooting and that he, Samaki, would take care of everything else.

The next afternoon, after the set lines were put out for the fish, the two African youths paddled for their rendezvous at different times so no one would know that they had gone out together. With their canoes

hidden in papyrus, they set out through rather open woods for the place on the veld where the water hole was hidden by green rushes and bushes. After the wooded banks of the channel, the country was rather open in places and they had to be alert so no would see them. A flight of marabou storks flew over them from left to right.

"Look," exclaimed Winda, "they go straight across our path as if to stop us. This is very bad luck." Samaki was worried, but tried to appear otherwise. "It was just a chance. Had we been coming from over there," he indicated a point of woods at an angle, "they would have crossed over our heads as if leading us to good luck."

Winda was unhappy about this explanation. He was still more unhappy when a dark brown snake crossed their path. This was a true sign of bad luck. He wanted to go back to the canoes, but just then a green snake slithered across their path. "Look," happily exclaimed Samaki, "this is good luck."

Winda wanted to argue that one sign of good luck did not cancel two signs of bad luck, but just then they saw something huge and gray coming their way.

The way in which that gray shape moved in a deliberate, swaying manner, showed only too plainly that it was the big elephant bull. Both young men were so excited that they forgot all about signs of good and bad luck.

Hurrying toward the water hole and the thicket where the bow and arrows were hidden, the two breathlessly awaited the approach of the elephant. Luckily for them, the wind was in their favor, blowing from the elephant to them. Elephants are smart enough to walk into the wind so they can scent danger ahead, but since they were not hunted here, they did not bother much about the wind directions.

Endoomy, the big one, strode through the high grass, his massive head rising and falling with each step. Going in advance of his small herd of cows and calves, he was on his way to the small water hole. Often, a wise old cow led the herd and Endoomy acted as rear guard. But lately lions which might harm some of the small elephants had been prowling about. This may have been Endoomy's reason for leading the herd today.

Endoomy came on, entirely unaware that death waited for him in a thicket of bushes near the water hole. He was also unaware that a big lion yawned and stretched in still another thicket. This lion had slept through the heat of the day. Now he wanted a drink. The great, tawny beast, mane blowing in the hot wind, strode boldly out to the water's muddy edge. There he lowered his muscular form to a crouch while he lapped the water.

The two conspirators saw the lion from their hiding place. This was something that they had not considered in their plans. Very much afraid of the big cat, they dared not move. Both knew that their poisoned arrows would not stop the charge of this lion. He might die later of the poison, but his claws and fangs would do their terrible work before he died. There was nothing to do but sit quietly and hope that the lion would go away.

On came the big elephant. As he came close to the water hole, he smelled the rank scent of the lion. Raising his trunk, he trumpeted an angry warning to the big cat.

Frozen into immobility, with all thought of ivory gone from their minds for the moment, Samaki and Winda watched the drama unfold before them.

Curling his trunk back out of the way of mauling claws, Endoomy advanced on the lion, rumbling angrily and with his long tusks pointed at the lion as if to impale him.

Sullenly snarling, the great yellow cat crouched as if debating about springing on the huge elephant. Then, coughing out an angry roar, the lion quickly turned about to bound into the very thicket where the now terror-stricken pair waited.

Screaming in wild alarm, the two would-be ivory poachers jumped to the right and left, as the lion landed in the bushes near them. They burst from the thicket as if the bushes had exploded and blown them forth. Abandoning bow and arrows, they raced for the channel and their hidden canoes. Both the lion and Endoomy looked surprised and bewildered, but made no attempt to follow the hunters in their mad flight.

Lakana, the sergeant of the game guards, accompanied by two of his helpers, had watched this whole scene from a distance. These guards had been strolling along watching the elephants go to water. Then they saw the lion jump away from the water hole, followed by Samaki and Winda fleeing wildly toward the channel.

It was too late in the day to do anything about this now, because the elephants might loiter at the water until dark, so the guards returned to their village for the night.

Early next morning, the guards set out for the water hole. Here the drama of the evening before unfolded itself readily for these men of nature. Here were the tracks in the mud made by the lion. There were the elephant's tracks as the big bull came toward the lion. There, too, were the tracks made by the young men as they ran away from the thicket. Inside the thicket, they found the abandoned bow and arrows. The arrows they handled with extreme care. They needed no one to tell them that the arrows were poisoned. Lakana took them to the game warden. He also told the warden the names of the two who had run from the thicket where the arrows were hidden.

It would be a long time before anyone again attempted to go poaching for Endoomy's ivory. The two young men were given a month in jail to ponder over their mistakes. Winda kept reminding Samaki about good-luck and bad-luck signs. He was sure that things had gone wrong because they had disregarded the signs. Now Samaki was sure about it, too. Old Emzay had not suffered because he had not taken part in the hunt.

Endoomy was busy in a thicket. He was tearing branches from trees to get at the tender end-shoots. He had never known how close he had come to losing his life when he had gone to the water hole. It had clouded up in the night and now a gentle rain fell. The yellow veld would soon be green and blossoming with flowers. Everywhere, there would be food and water for wild folks. Endoomy rumbled with content.

2:

The

Phantom

Hunter

It was one of those stygian-black tropical nights. Despite the darkness, creatures moved about at their nightly affairs. The multitude of fanged and clawed beasts that inhabit the African veld prefer to promote their nefarious deeds under cover of darkness. Hyenas moaned and wailed; a jackal yapped back in high-keyed derision; and from the forest's edge, a leopard coughed harshly in his wood-sawing manner, *"Uh-ha-r-r, uh-har-r-r!"*

Genet paused to sniff at the trail, trying to separate the many scents that crossed and crisscrossed each other. He looked much like a marten with spots, but was related to the civets. He had a catlike face, with slit pupils in his eyes, but his nose was a bit too pointed for a cat. Also his legs were short in proportion to the length of his body. He was grayish brown, with many dark brown streaks, spots and blotches. Like the civets, he had a musty odor.

In the midst of his sniffing about, Genet gave a sudden start and executed a move between a back somersault and a corkscrew dive. This landed him securely under thorn-studded branches, just as something struck the spot where he had been a split second before. Great needle-sharp talons left pointed marks in the dusty trail. There was an odd clicking sound. Then the thing, whatever it was, silently dissolved into the darkness whence it had come.

Genet spat out a catlike sound at the night's blackness. Then he heard the alarmed sneezing of the impala and the quick tapping of their sharp hoofs, as, panic-stricken, they fled in long leaps. The alarmed hurrying of a herd of small gazelles next smote on his senses. He pricked up his ears and wrinkled his nose as he heard the faint bleating of a gazelle kid. The phantom killer of the night was abroad.

Ever since he had been a soft-furred genet kitten, following his mother about these trails, Genet had made this place his home. Hunting was good in this bush and forest country. There was a lake not far away and every manner of bird and beast from miles around came here to drink. It was a great place for hunters like Genet. Although he was but eighteen inches long, including his long, ringed tail, Genet was a hunter among hunters. In comparison to size, he was perhaps a more deadly hunter than many large beasts of prey. Some people called him "Genet cat," but his real name was genet, as he was not a member of the cat family.

Chiefly, Genet hunted mice, rats, birds, and other small veld inhabitants. He often caught insects on the jump, for he could jump twice his length into the air in capturing them. There was little peril attendant on his hunting, except that he had constantly to be on the alert from being hunted by larger beasts. Any of the larger clawed and fanged hunters that lived here would gladly have snuffed out his life.

Genet's exceeding swiftness stood him in good stead. Many a beast had pounced on him from ambush only to find that they had pounced upon nothing. He had contrived to be some other place than the spot on which they landed with outspread claws.

But, of late, some sinister menace had invaded his favorite hunting grounds. Three times it had struck at him and each time he had escaped by just inches. One time it had been just a fraction of an inch. A mate had been taken at his very side while the two were out hunting.

He had looked about for her, but she had been whisked away as if she had dissolved into the night air. Each time, he had heard a sharp, clicking sound, as if two dry bones were struck together. Aside from this, there had been silence — no hurrying of padded feet, no striking of claws on stone, no scent on the earth to give him a clue. One of the most nervously alert of this bushveld, he was more so after these experiences, ever ready to execute a double-quick disappearing act.

Genet had no more than set out on the trail again after the last alarm, when he quickly jack-knifed to one side to make way for an old male banded mongoose. This one hurried along the trail in long, bounding jumps, snarling through bared teeth at each jump. Here was something strange, for this mongoose was anything but a coward. Genet sniffed as the mongoose hurried past. His keen nose told him that there was blood on the mongoose's banded coat — blood of his own and not that of one of his victims.

A big-eared fox went past, furtively and swiftly, as though a demon was at his heels. At the lake's edge, the impala were nervously snorting, "P-r-r, p-r-r, p-r-r!" Again, the leopard coughed, "Uh-har-r!"

Pocketing his nervousness, Genet made his way to an acacia grove, where he soon was streaking up a tree trunk. His nose had told him that he would find some plump quail-like francolin roosting here. The scent led him to where a half dozen were asleep. He leaped upon the nearest. The others, awakened at its strangled cry, rocketed away into the night on booming wings to find other roosts as best they could.

Soon Genet saw that another beast was crouched upon a nearby branch. Genet's nose told him that this was one of his own kind. At once, he was all abristle, mewing like a cat, for he had no intention of sharing this meal. Then he sensed that this was a female Genet and he changed his aggressive attitude, edging to one side and purring an invitation.

For a time, the female Genet crouched in distrust of him. Then, gliding close, she fiercely grasped one foot of the francolin in her teeth and pulled it toward her. Genet spat at her for this unladylike behavior. Sinking his sharp teeth in the francolin's neck, he hung on doggedly while she jerked and pulled. Thus — one on each end of the unfortunate bird — hissing, snarling, and mewing, they ate their meal.

The lady Genet seemed to take for granted this meal that he had

W.J.Wilwerding

furnished. She was no more inclined toward friendliness when she was finished than when she had at first invited herself to the repast. She whisked down the tree, with Genet following swiftly at her heels. He had been without a mate for some time and here was his opportunity to acquire a new one. He had difficulty in following her trail.

Her trail took him through one maze of thorn-bowered galleries after another. Then, for a space, he followed it in more open country. He was tripping along in the rapid, undulating manner of his kind, when he suddenly realized that he had overrun her trail. Retracing his steps, he followed her trail again. Once more he overran it in his eagerness to catch up with her. He went back again to sniff out her trail. This time, he patiently set his nose to it and followed along. Now the reason for his having overrun her trail raced excitedly through his fiery brain. The trail suddenly ended — it did not carry on! Something was very, very wrong here. He raced back and forth, vainly trying to pick up her trail again. He hunched his spotted back; his nose wove nervously back and forth — sniffing, sniffing.

Perhaps some other beast had come along and blotted out her trail. Perhaps she had made a wide jump in avoiding some peril. Perhaps he would pick up her trail again farther on. He searched and he sniffed, but her trail had ended forever. He went on with his mind in a red daze.

He came to an African compound of huts. Snooping about near the outskirts, he came to a little spot between a ring of thorn branches where he smelled the head of a chicken. Feeling impelled to sniff further into this business, he stepped forward. *Snap* — something fastened on his foot, biting tightly into it. He jerked back on the instant he had felt something give, but, despite his quickness, it had caught his toes. Furiously, he bit at the thing, finding it hard, cold and unyielding to his teeth. He could in no way pull his toes loose. It came along with him when he pulled. Something was fastened to one end of it which rattled loudly in a metallic manner. The Africans had fastened an empty can to the chain on the end of the trap. Genet hissed and snarled, biting the trap again and again in his desperation, until his lips were raw and bleeding.

There can hardly be a worse place and time to be caught in a trap than in Africa at night. Usually, the one who sets the trap to rid himself of predators that come to steal his chickens finds the trap empty in the morning. This is not because the miserable victim got loose, but because others have come along and made a meal of him.

A pattering of feet advertised the fact that one of these was on his way to end Genet's worries. Genet's keen nostrils told him that his visitor was a jackal. He knew that he could expect no quarter from this sharp-eared, sharp-nosed, and sharp-fanged wild dog. But Genet prepared to fight for his life, baring his teeth to sink them into his enemy's nose. The jackal stopped a few feet away. The combination of the odor of the fowl's head, the scent of steel, and the musky smell of Genet, made him pause and try to figure this thing out before coming too close.

For a few moments the jackal turned this conglomeration of smells over in his foxlike head. Then, deciding that it was safe to proceed, he lunged at Genet with a snap of fangs. Something else had seen Genet in the trap and pounced at the same moment. But the jackal's head had been in the way just then and it caught at the jackal's head. Something was sticking sharp needles in his head and the jackal leaped back with shrill yelps of alarm. Genet had given the jackal one quick bite on the nose, just as this other thing had intervened. Genet doubled back and managed somehow to drag the trap under the protection of thornbushes. Having had enough of this business, the jackal had already left the scene. Again, Genet had heard the faint clicking sound as the thing had descended on the jackal's head.

Genet was racking his small brain for some means of getting rid of this thing that clung to his foot, when a nasty, gibbering gang of hyenas came to visit him. One lunged forward with a chop of fangs that would have neatly taken a man's hand off at the wrist. But Genet had managed to drag the trap farther underneath the thorns. In place of genet meat, the hyena got thorns in his blunt, black muzzle. He swore throatily at the pain.

Then the hyena set to scratching with one heavy forefoot to drag Genet forth. The rest of his crew stood back, making all the unearthly racket of which they were capable. Genet would have been just a mouthful for any one of these, but hyenas do not think of this when out hunting.

Things looked black for Genet. If the hyena caught his claws on the trap's chain and pulled it forth, Genet would be finished. But just then the hyena happened to place his heavy foot on the spring of the trap.

24

Feeling something under his foot, he pressed down to drag it out. Genet, straining back to keep out of reach, suddenly felt the jaws of the trap open and he pulled free. The next moment he had vanished along a thorny aisle under the bushes, a trail that smaller creatures used to avoid large four-footed evils.

When, after much more stupid scratching, the hyena finally dragged the trap forth, there were only a few of Genet's hairs sticking to the jaws and the bait of the chicken's head tied to the pan. A very small lunch for the pains he had taken.

The trap had done Genet's foot no good. He favored it as he went along the trail. He had but one thought in mind now, to get to some safe retreat where he could rest and nurse his sore foot. He came to a big, twisted-branched umbrella-acacia tree to which his unerring sense of direction had taken him. He scampered up the rough bark, seeking a snug place he knew of in the hollow of a big limb. About to enter this hollow, some sixth sense warned him to draw back. In the next atom of time, he doubled back, quick as an electric spark, springing to another branch, just as a slender tree mamba struck at him.

Genet crouched motionless for a moment, watching intently for the deadly snake's next move. Then he saw that something else had seen the snake's movements and had dropped silently to fasten upon it. Too late this hunter of the night saw his great mistake — too late to stop his silent plunge. He had seen Genet go up the tree and had thought to catch him. The movements of the snake's head had fooled him and he had caught seven feet of fanged death in his talons.

Needle-sharp talons sought quickly to cut the life out of the deadly serpent, but the head of that sinuous form had already flashed forward and done its deadly work. Talons pierced the mamba's vitals, even as the snake struck, but the fangs had gone home. For a short time, Genet heard a snapping and clicking. Then serpent and hunter, turning over and over in their fall to earth, lay in a quivering mass on the hard ground below.

Genet had flattened to the branch during these tense moments. Now he somehow knew that the silent menace of the night had robbed him of his last mate and would bother him no more. He proceeded to his home in the hollow, where dawn, peeping in through the leaves, found him curled up in sleep.

"It is a large owl, bwana, a very large owl," exclaimed Watindo, my gunbearer, when I asked him to see what manner of bird lay under the tree we were passing in the early African dawn. Stepping close to inspect the bird, I saw that it was a milky eagle owl, a rare bird even in its native habitat. Its eyes were dark instead of yellow, like those of his cousin the great horned owl of America. Even in death, the big bird had a fearsome and defiant look. It was easy to see how it had met its death, for it still clutched the dead mamba in its talons.

We passed that way again later in the day to find that the daytime hunters of Africa had been at work there. The mamba had been eaten almost entirely, except for its deadly head. Where the great owl had lain, a mass of gray feathers were blowing about, even as this tiger among birds had floated on his nightly raids — silently, save for the angry snapping of his beak.

3: Muishond's Revenge

Muishond did not like the hot sun, or perhaps it was that most of the small creatures he hunted went abroad only at night. Anyway, here he was shuffling along a dusty trail in the early darkness of the African night. Had it been light, you would have seen a little black and white animal that looked much like an American skunk, but with a longer tail in proportion to its body. His tail was three quarters of the length of his head and body. The soles of his feet were hairy, not bare as on a skunk. He was only about fifteen inches long from the tip of his weasel-like nose to the root of his long, white tail. *Muis-hond* was the name the South African settlers had given him. This described his main diet, for, translated, it means "mouse-dog." Some were not quite so charitable in naming him and frankly called him *"steenk-kat,"* which means "stink-cat." Both names described him very well, for besides being an industrious hunter of mice, he could raise such a stink (which was his main defense) that African tribes to the north called him "father of all stinks."

His scent glands were near the root of his tail. It may be dainty to say that it was a scent, but it was the granddaddy of all the bad smells on earth when he let go with both barrels, or, to be more correct, with both scent glands. He could eject this oily, volatile fluid from one or the other scent gland at will. He let them both go, like the two barrels of a shotgun, when the emergency was immediate and great. He had a very precise aim and those who disturbed him went away very much disturbed themselves. Also, they smelled to high heaven for many days.

To see him walking prettily along the game trail, all dressed up in his black and white evening clothes, you would not be aware that he carried such a malodorous defense weapon. But you should be most fully forewarned, since Nature has marked most of her stinkards by giving them black coats with white stripes or spots. So, even if you don't know one of these pretty little beasts from another and happen to see one in a strange land — the black and white coat will serve as a warning.

Muishond was a zoril, or African polecat. His kind are found all over Africa except in the deepest forests. They like rocky places. Muishond had his den in a cleft between big rocks and this was his castle. From here he set out on forays into the surrounding bush country. He did all his hunting on the ground, as he did not climb trees. In the tall grass, he found grasshoppers. He also licked up ants and their larvae. He wasn't too particular about what he ate. Insects, beetles, grubs, birds' eggs, lizards, frogs, snakes, mice, and rats were food to him.

He came to a small African village of mud and wattle huts. Here he scented the musty smell of roosting chickens. He sniffed about until he found a small opening that led inside a hut. His nose quickly told him where the fowl were kept. Gleefully, he slew a number, before the alarmed cackling of the others awakened the Africans. These took staffs and spears and went to drive the intruder away. Muishond went out through the same opening that had provided his entrance, but not before he had left his worst regards. There was no more sleeping in that hut for the rest of the night. Muishond's air spray would hardly have been called "Rose Delight."

Muishond went poking along, sniffing at this place and that. He stopped to tear at a rotting log on the ground. Here he was rewarded with grubs of beetles. He found a tall termites' mound of red clay. Digging inside, he made a lunch of the termites.

Then, shuffling along, he flushed a francolin from her nest in the grass. This chickenlike bird flew away with a harsh, alarmed cackle. She was lucky to have escaped with her life. Muishond did not mind catching birds of this size for a meal. He was not really hungry any

more and was just poking about at his hunting from habit. He ate one egg and was licking up the yolk when a jackal smelled the broken egg and came to share the meal. Angrily, Muishond stamped his stiffened forefeet, making a small hissing sound that might have passed as a growl. This was his way of giving warning, as if to say, "Keep away or I'll let you have it!" Along with this, he raised his white tail aloft. With him, this was not a flag of truce, but a most definite warning that there was going to be a big stink. The jackal took one look and one sniff at what was eating an egg there in the grass and quickly went away.

Once, when he was young and ignorant, this jackal had tried to rob a zoril of a guinea fowl that it had caught. That had been his time for learning about a little black and white animal that does not run away. It had just turned its back and raised its tail. The jackal had made the mistake of reaching forth to snap at it. Something awful had happened to him then. A burning spray had filled his eyes, nose, and mouth. For a time he could not see where he went. He lay rolling over and over, rubbing his head in the grass to rid himself of this smarting thing. Tears washed away the fluid from his eyes so he was able to see again, but his scenting powers were gone for the night, and he had gone hungry.

Because most creatures needed but one lesson to learn about Muishond's weapon of defense, he did not have to resort to it very often. Mostly he walked about entirely unconcerned about the larger beasts that he encountered on his nightly hunts. Most animals stepped aside for him.

Of course, there are always those who won't take a dare and others who have not had their lesson as yet and must go through their first experience. One night Muishond had gone out hunting with his mate. While he had been busy catching mice, she had caught a nesting guinea fowl. A big spotted hyena had come lumbering along and found her at her meal. Evilly cackling, he snapped at the meal she was eating. She gave him both barrels straight in the eyes. Blinded and with nostrils and mouth burning as if afire, he snapped her up and shook the life out of her. Then he whined and scooted his nose in the grass to rub off this substance that so sorely bothered him. But Muishond's mate lay dead and the whole wild world smelled it on the wind that night.

A few nights later, Muishond came to a place surrounded by thornbushes where a big thickly maned lion lay leisurely at his meal. This lion was feeding on a brindled gnu that he had caught for his dinner. Jackals and hyenas lurked about in a surrounding circle, looking like gray ghouls in the light of the moon. This crew watched for a chance to dart in, grab some meat and run. Thwarted in this, they would wait until the lion finished and went away to drink. Then they would very quickly devour what he had left.

Muishond looked and sniffed at this assemblage of carrion eaters, all giants compared to him. Had it not been night, you might have detected a gleam of disdain in his beady eyes. Without stopping in his stride, he walked right through this motley crowd of beasts, white tail held aloft in dire warning. They took one look at him and made way for him, as if some nobleman of the wild were entering the glade. Muishond walked right up to where the lion was feeding. This big beast took one quick look at what had come to join him at dinner. Then, flat-eared and furiously rumbling a deep-throated growl, the lion backed away. This fellow knew all about these little black and white animals that walked up close with such studied nonchalance. Now the lion shed his kingly manners while he crouched at a little distance to watch Muishond eat.

Seeing that the lion had backed away from his meal, one big hulking hyena — the same one that had killed Muishond's mate — darted in to bite off a piece of meat. In his great greed, he had apparently forgotten what had happened to him a few nights before. The stench of the encounter with Muishond's mate was still with him. But then, no one expects a hyena to smell sweet. When he made the mistake of getting too close to Muishond, this little fellow gave him both barrels. Yammering, with the smarting fluid in his eyes, the hyena stumbled away, backing directly into the lion. One furious growl and one tremendous slap with a huge claw-armed paw and the hyena quit this thorny wilderness forever. Muishond had been avenged for the loss of his mate, but it is doubtful that he was aware of this. He only knew that the hyena no longer bothered him.

It did not take Muishond long to fill up, as there was much meat and his stomach was small. Full of food, he had no further need to go hunting this night. He had wandered rather far from his home den on this night's foray. Being fully fed and a bit drowsy, he did not turn his steps homeward, but crept into a thorn thicket and slept. Perhaps he dreamed that he was conquering giants.

4: Tall Friend and Ally

It was early September in the high veld country of central Tanganyika. The long dry season had cracked the parched black earth between the bunches of brittle yellow veld grass. A midday sun mercilessly glared down out of a brassy sky, sending heat vibrations shimmering over the seared veld. These vibrations bent with the wind as if steam escaped from every grass root. The dazzling glare made the whole vast veld dance and quiver.

A herd of two dozen giraffes, walking from one acacia grove to another, appeared like some fantastic beasts out of a nightmare. Their long necks and legs looked twisted and contorted with the heat vibrations as they sedately walked along. Even the little Thomson's gazelles appeared to be writhed and twirled into vaporous shapes, in this all-enveloping shimmer arising from the heat-tortured earth.

Tommy, the little goatlike leader of the gazelle herd, seemed to pay little attention to the furnacelike heat of noonday. When other veld creatures, the zebras, gnus, and kongonis, had sought the meager shade provided by scattered thorn trees, the little gazelle grazed in the open with his herd. A few lay down in the grass to rest, while others fed on the cured hay provided by nature for their sustenance.

Tommy looked about, both to make sure that no danger approached and that no rival gazelle buck would come to steal one of his does from the herd. There were over thirty gazelles in this herd; some does with very small young, and others of all growing sizes.

Tommy was a dapper, nattily dressed little fellow. He was two feet high at the shoulders and was russet-tan on the back and sides, which color was sharply cut off from the snow-white of his belly by a broad black band that slanted downward a bit from rear to forequarters, making it appear as if he were higher toward the rear. Black, ringed horns curved backward from above his eyes. His sharply pointed ears were held forward and alert, while his black tail went round and round in a continual twirling wag. He seemed to be keeping time with other members of his herd, whose tails everlastingly wagged with his. In spite of their bold black side stripes and those busily wagging tails, their tan colors blended well with the colors of the veld at a little distance, and one might not have been aware that gazelles grazed there. With the heat vibrations breaking up their forms, it took a second look to discover them.

Tommy's attention was on his tall friends, the giraffes. He watched these fellows closely as they stalked along. He knew that they could sight danger from afar, while he and his kind stood barely above the grass in height and could not readily detect any sneakers who might stalk them. Because of this, he rarely grazed his herd far from the sight of giraffes. Should anything suspicious cause the giraffes to stampede, he snorted the alarm call and away his herd went on the jump. Usually they ran close to the tails of the giraffes.

Tommy and his herd were very fleet-footed. Even a greyhound would have difficulty keeping up with them. They mainly feared the cheetah. He was one of their arch enemies. This long-legged, spotted cat hunted them like a greyhound, except that no greyhound on earth could keep pace with him. When he took off, other beasts looked as if they were tied. This light yellow cheetah could crouch down in the grass and make himself invisible. Unfortunately for the little gazelles, he too was a creature of the open veld. One never knew when the grass would suddenly erupt with a cheetah that was coming at full gallop.

Others also hunted gazelles. The serval cat at times pounced upon a small one or he would run one down like the cheetah. Jackals and hyenas also took toll of the young. Now and again, a big crowned hawk-eagle swooped and took a young one. So Tommy had learned to be everlastingly alert. Watchfulness in the wild was the price of safety. One used one's nose, one's eyes, one's ears. One watched the birds to see what might have alarmed them. One kept one's large, lustrous gazelle's eyes on the tall giraffes, knowing that they saw far and wide.

The giraffes stopped to feed in some tall yellow-barked acacia trees. These trees stood in a decorative group on the western border of the grassland. As the giraffes busied themselves with plucking the tender top shoots of these trees, Tommy and his herd drifted near them. It was always best to be close to the giraffes when one was just a little gazelle. Every now and then one of the giraffes stopped feeding to look about and then walked in a stately manner to sample the products of another tree.

A big giraffe bull looked down at Tommy as he walked close. Tommy went right up to the big fellow and looked up at him. Lowering his large head, the giraffe touched noses with Tommy. They were old veld friends and saw each other every day. Most of the hoofed creatures of this land were friendly toward others, whether large or small. Zebras at times came to graze near the giraffes, as did impala, kongoni, and gnus. Even the ostriches came to join these herds and to graze with them. In company, these animals found safety. With many eyes, ears and noses continually on the watch, there was a greater measure of security than when one depended solely on one's own senses.

Sometimes, a big old gnu bull came to join the herd of gazelles, standing darkly in their midst while they fed all around him. This old gnu was very wise from years of living on the veld and also very alert for any possible danger. With him standing there on guard, the gazelles could feed without worry of anything stalking them.

Tommy also depended on birds to warn him and his kind of any nearby danger. The only unfriendly birds were those big, brown eagles that now and then swooped to catch a young gazelle. There was nothing that the gazelles could do about this. The smaller birds, having to keep alert themselves, were quick in sounding the alarm when something crouched, sneaked or skulked nearby. Then all shrieked the news for the whole wild world to hear.

Tommy and his herd grazed in the grass not far from where the giraffes fed in the acacias. They loafed about at their feeding and resting until late in the afternoon, when the giraffes became restless. The day had been long and hot and it was time to go and get a drink. All the small water holes had dried up long ago, but there was a small lake not far away. They could walk from the acacia groves through a dried-out swamp in which the dried and dead rushes still stood. A much-trodden trail led through here to the shore of the lake. Here many water

and wading birds swarmed and a herd of hippopotamuses snorted.

The giraffes had started to walk out of the grove when a black-headed yellow oriole mewed like a cat. This warning cry was at once taken up by other birds. The giraffes curled up their tails and ran past the gazelles. The gazelles at once set out on the heels of the giraffes as these big beasts went away in their long, rocking gallop.

A leopard, out hunting early, had been sneaking through the thicket to pounce on a gazelle. But the birds had warned the giraffes and the giraffes had warned the gazelles. The leopard stood, baffled, at the edge of the thicket, with the yellow light flaring in his eyes. He looked up at the screaming birds and it appeared as if he muttered something to them, no doubt entirely uncomplimentary. By this time, the giraffes were already near the water, with the gazelles close by.

It was on an early dewy morning, after one of the first showers of the rainy days, with the smell of earth and blossoms on the morning air, when Tommy looked up from grazing to see something that did not look quite right. A thorn tree stood at the edge of the dried-out swamp with its lower gracefully drooping branches brushing the grass tops. This tree grew very full for a thorn tree. It was fully leafed and in blossom. Tommy knew this tree very well, as he knew all the trees, bushes, rocks, and other features of the landscape about him. This was his home and he was acquainted with it, as a person knows the furniture in his own house. This morning, there was something wrong about this tree. Tommy sniffed the air, but the breeze was away from him toward the tree and it brought him no news. His ears told him nothing, as there was no strange sound. But his eyes did not lie to him and these told him that there was something hiding in this tree. He could see shadows in the lower part, near the trunk, that did not belong there. He walked

up for a closer look. There certainly was something in there.

Now all the gazelles had their heads up and were on the alert. Many eyes looked at the deep shadow in the lower part of the tree. They seemed puzzled and they stared and stared, waiting for something to move, but nothing moved. When one is a Wairamba hunter out to shoot a giraffe with bow and arrows, one knows better than to move and one also is sure that the wind is blowing from the game and not to it. This morning, there were two such hunters hiding in the tree, as it was thick with branches and leaves and provided good cover. But here those little gazelles had come tripping along just as the giraffes were coming through the old swamp on their way from the lake and their morning drink.

Tommy kept looking at those shadows. He seemed uncertain about his next move. His herd stood waiting his signal. Just then a lilac-breasted roller (a bird somewhat like a bluejay in size and form) flew into the thorn tree with his tumbling flight. His very sharp eyes looked down. They saw something that he did not like and he sounded off with a harsh "Jay!" Tommy needed no further information. His snort brought his herd into action. Tommy ran toward the approaching giraffes, his whole herd in flight with him.

The giraffes, with lowered heads, were feeding on the leaves of low bushes as they walked along. Now they quickly raised their heads. They, too, needed no further information when they saw the gazelles come full tilt at them. Turning about, they led the gazelles in flight, leaving the disappointed hunters behind. The giraffes had not seen the hunters, as, from their height, they had looked down on the thorn tree. Tommy could see under the lower branches. So, with the help of the bird, the short helped the tall when danger was nigh.

Now the grass grew green from the rain. Where there had only been dead grass, the green veld was dotted with colorful wild flowers. There

were pools of water in every depression. One did not have to wander far for water. Birds sang and the trees were hung with the little round dried-grass nests of the weaver finches. Tommy was out in the open grass. All the gazelles were busily grazing and switching their tails — which must have been a nervous habit, for their little short tails were no good at switching away insects.

Tommy reached forth with one little black hind hoof to scratch the back of his ear on that side. A bothersome tick was biting him. He raised his head to look about, and right then it appeared as if this would be the last time that he would see his herd and the blossoming veld of the East African spring. Certain death was coming straight at him — a cheetah at full gallop.

There are not many things that can run faster than a gazelle, but the cheetah is one of these. This long-legged, round-spotted yellow cat can outrun anything that runs on the African veld. Tommy knew that fate was bearing down on him, but he grunted a warning to his herd. As these scattered before the oncoming beast, he streaked across the grass in a desperate attempt to outrun his foe. In a long run he might have succeeded, for the cheetah has no staying powers. But in the first burst of speed of the cheetah, nothing on earth can outrun him.

Tommy heard the hurried footbeats behind him, as he strained muscles to outrun this certain disaster. The cheetah gained readily and was almost upon him, when Tommy suddenly saw the giraffe herd directly in front of him. From instinct or perhaps previous experience in depending on these tall allies of his in time of danger, he ran directly at the giraffes, darting under the lead bull as the cheetah was closing in on him.

The big bull giraffe took one startled look at what had come running. He reared up and sent two big forehoofs smashing down on the cheetah's back. This ended the cheetah's hunting days. Looking very insulted and dignified, the giraffe looked down at the still form of the cheetah and walked stiffly away.

Tommy circled about and found his herd. Soon vultures soared above. These always have the last word, or last bite, after the wild hunters are through with their work, or when the bitter time comes to the wild hunter himself. Tommy watched the vultures as they dropped to earth with wings spread and landing gear down. He wagged his little black tail.

5: Big Ears

Out on the wide, grassy, rolling East African veld, where the earth sloped a bit in a high place that gave a good view all about, Big Ears and his little big-eared mate had their den. Big Ears was a little great-eared fox, smaller than the common fox and of a grizzled-gray color. He had blackish legs, a bushy tail with a black tip, and perfectly enormous ears. His kind are remarkable for having more molar teeth than most of the other mammals on earth. Often, four of these grow in each jaw. Big Ears perhaps needed all these teeth for masticating the termites and other insects that he ate.

Big Ears and his mate usually began their hunting forays toward dusk and did most of their hunting in the night. During the day, the two often sat on guard near the den's entrance. They had a good reason for this — there were four little woolly cubs in the den. As they sat at this high place on watch, they could see their veld neighbors scattered about in all directions. White-bearded gnus honked, gaudily striped zebras barked, and tan-colored impala rams snorted in their odd, purring manner. These had large harems of females that looked like graceful doe deer.

The fox parents sat at the den's entrance to decoy away anyone who might come near the den to disturb their young. At any sign of the approach of a person or any other creature, the pair scuttled off, circling about to lure the intruder away.

A day came when the cubs were huddled together at the den's dark mouth, lying so close as to appear like one furry animal with four heads. Now their parents were especially watchful. A big baboon walked close. He was as large as a retriever dog, olive-colored and tough. Big Ears and his mate at once began circling about at a distance, whistling to their young, who came scampering. All of them now huddled down in the grass at some distance to watch the baboon. It is doubtful that the baboon was out hunting for little foxes, but how were they to tell what an old baboon might do or what he might want to eat? Now he hunted for grasshoppers in the grass. After this big dog-faced monkey had gone to join his fellows, who were hunting in the grass not far away, the little foxes went back to their burrow.

While the cubs were still too young to go hunting with Big Ears and his mate, the two older foxes went out hunting for the family. Though their teeth were too small to catch large game, they hunted mice and birds to take home to the den. Digging into termite mounds, they filled their stomachs with the white termites. Between the two foxes, they often ate two quarts of termites in a night.

Big Ears often hunted for mice and other rodents in the grass. He was as adept as a cat at this, catching little harvest mice and small striped mice. He waited in ambush near the colonies of burrows dug by the little pygmy gerbilles. He caught these as they came forth to hunt for food and play about near their burrows. These looked like little kangaroo rats, but were no larger than mice. When hunting was good, Big Ears lined his mouth with small rodents to take home to the cubs.

As the cubs grew, the old pair took them hunting. To show the young how to find their own food, Big Ears dug into the mound of red earth that the termites had built as their castle. Whistling to the young, as an old hen clucks to her chicks, he showed them where the termites swarmed. It did not take them long to learn that by digging into these mounds they could find food for themselves. This was a never-failing supply of food and when other hunting was bad they could always live on termites.

So, day by day, or rather, night by night, the young cubs learned how one caught insects, mice, and other small things that meant food and life for little big-eared foxes.

All was going well until, one day, a serval cat found the den. This old she-serval, who looked somewhat like a bobcat but whose tail was longer, had young of her own to feed. She sniffed around at the den's entrance, found that there was life inside, and crouched down in the grass to wait for the young to emerge. The older foxes had scampered off at her approach. Now they warily circled about, not daring to whistle to the young lest they come forth and run into the waiting serval. Foxes were not the serval's regular prey, but with young to feed, any meat would do. She was big and yellow-eyed and one of the wily hunters of the grass country.

Big Ears went close so she could see him. She pounced at him, and he quickly darted to one side to escape her mad rush. He repeated this maneuver as she stalked him. Thus, he drew her farther and farther away from the den. She was very fast, but he was quicker and could outrun her. Warily, he watched her every movement, preferring to out-wit her than to try to outrun her. So, alternately watching her and darting aside as she came at him, he managed to get her far from the den. In the meantime, his mate circled back to the den, whistled up the young, and took them away to a safe place. Big Ears now ran away from the serval. Later, by circling about and whistling, he made contact with his mate and family.

After this experience, realizing that the scent of the old den advertised the fact that the young were there, the parents hunted for a new den. They dug out a place that an aardvark had started for them. This piglike anteater had been digging for ants in the night and his digging had started a very good den for the little foxes. They dug deeper to make a safe place for the young. This would provide for their young a new, clean place that the serval would not know about. They knew the persistence of the cats and that they never forgot a place where hunting was good. The serval certainly would return to the old den.

Before the old foxes could move their young to the new den, a leopard who just happened to be passing that way sniffed out the knowledge that the old den held cubs. The big spotted cat had been

42

disappointed in his baboon hunting early this evening. The baboons had been on their way to their roosting place in a grove of thorn trees when they encountered the leopard. The tough old advance guards were so numerous and put up such a formidable front that the leopard dared not attack. Now he had gone seeking other game. So here he found a foxes' den, and apparently they were at home. Leopards are fond of dog meat and will go out of their way to catch a dog. These little foxes were much like little dogs. They are called *"octoyon,"* which is Greek and means "eared dog."

The leopard sniffed about at the den's entrance and then he crouched down and began digging. Leopards usually are not given to digging out their game the way wild dogs do, but this one found the earth soft, and he dug at it. Having enlarged the entrance, he poked a clawed paw down into the hole to see if he could hook out a cub.

Big Ears and his mate were watching the leopard from a distance. Now they were frantic and circled close, hoping to lure the big cat away. But the leopard paid no attention to them. He probably knew how active these little foxes were and that he would have trouble in catching them. It would be far easier to dig out the cubs. He kept scratching away, enlarging the hole. Soon he got well down into it. He thrust a big paw far into the den, almost to the rear of the den, where the young had retreated. After a bit more digging, he would have the hole so enlarged that he could readily hook out the young, one by one. The leopard knew that he had found a cache of live food, and he was determined to get it.

Big Ears and his mate circled very close now. Despairingly, they made little whimpering sounds, hopelessly trying to lure the leopard away from their young. This spotted fellow had now dug his way down to where his claws were within inches of the huddled cubs. Resignation now seemed to take the place of despair in the fox pair. Mournfully, they now sat on their haunches whimpering, the anguish of their vigil showing in their large lustrous eyes. The moon looked down out of the cold sky to light the scene with its merciless light, while the leopard gave a last few scratches that would put the cubs at his mercy. But what was this noise? The veld rumbled with the quick pounding of many wild hoofs.

At once, Big Ears and his mate were alert. The pounding of hoofbeats came closer — then, zebras and gnus streaked out of the night. The fox pair quickly sought safety in the entrance of a warthog's burrow. The leopard, head and shoulders down into the foxes' den, felt the vibration of the pounding hoofs. Hurriedly, he backed out. Swiftly he bounded away. He just barely found refuge in a thorn tree as the stampeding herds swept past.

The hoofed herds had been stampeded by hunting lions. As the alarm abated, the hoofed ones quieted down to resume their grazing. Now the leopard turned his attention to trying to catch a calf of the gnu herd. Stealthily, Big Ears and his mate returned to the dug-out den. Whistling their young to them, they quickly took them away to the new den. There they rested for a bit, letting the young get acquainted with their new home. Then they all set out on the hunt, for this is the way of the wild; life lives on life; one creature is food for another. Here, life and death forever walk side by side. Big Ears had learned this and so had his mate. The cubs, if they survived the perils that roamed these wilds and grew to maturity, would learn it too, in time. Already they were having daily lessons from the old pair. Mice squeaked, the foxes pricked their ears, and the hunt was on.

6: Jungle Wile

It was evening in East Africa. A red sun was sinking in the west. The ice and snow lay glistening in a bath of rose color on Kibo, the highest peak of Kilimanjaro mountain. Already, the forested mountainsides were purple with enveloping shadows. The sun dipped lower and the shadows reached upward with clutching fingers to extinguish Kibo's borrowed light.

At the forest's lower edge, where the tangled bush country blended forest with grassy plains, a lion sent out his rumbling roar. It vibrated and echoed through the night-conquered wilderness, as if a mighty master of ceremonies had sent forth a thunderous summons to arouse the night carnivores and warn the timid who were still abroad.

A hyena wailed a moaning, sirenlike reply, a jackal yapped, and back in the forest's secret shadows, a leopard coughed, *"Uh-harr-r, uh-harr-r!"* Then, save for the threnody of shrilling insects, there was quiet for a time. This quiet was suddenly broken by a quavering yowl, a caterwaul not to be mistaken whether heard in Africa's wilds or on the back fence in a city. Prowler, the African bush cat, was on the prowl. So closely did he resemble our fireside tabbies that one might have been impelled to call "Kitty!" to him on meeting him in the African bush country.

Prowler was of the size of a domestic cat. He was yellowish gray in color, with tabby markings on head, neck, body, and legs. He flaunted a ringed tail. Descendants of his ancestors, domesticated and revered in Egypt, were brought to Europe by conquering Romans. Proud, independent, self-contained, the domestic descendants of African bush cats have retained their original nature through the centuries. They hunt for the love of hunting, even when well fed, obtain their food and a soft place to sleep by cajolery, and bend in service to no man.

Prowler was by nature a lone hunter, given to consorting with none of his kind when on the hunt, for he who lives by stealth had better hunt alone. True, his hunting methods were ruthless, and he was no doubt bloodthirsty, but he lived as Nature meant that he should live. She had made him an eater of flesh and had armed him well for the task of obtaining it. To him, above all things, Nature had given the gift of great patience. If all the patience of all the beasts on earth were molded into one, it would only find its match in the possession of the little wild cat that roams in the African bush.

Nature had neglected to give Prowler the scenting powers of the wild dog, so he could not track his prey. She had forgotten to give him enduring speed, so he could not run down his prey. She may even have been a bit careless about his size. But Nature always makes amends and so she had given him this gift of great patience, without which his claws would be of no avail. Lacking patience, he might have perished.

Prowler wove in and out among the tangled mass of interwoven branches of the thicket that was his home. That he did not skin his nose at every step in the all-enveloping blackness of the night was due to the wonderful pupils in his eyes, which opened wide at night to give him sight in darkness. Also, his long whiskers were attached to sensitive nerves. These felt the way for him as a man holds his hands before him to avoid bumping into things in the dark.

Now and again, Prowler stood motionless, listening, for he had keen ears. Then, lightly and silently, he flitted along the trail, if that trackless maze he trod could be called one. He advertised his coming with a yowling *"E-yow-r-r-row-uh!"* This was not usual for him while hunting, but he was not now on the hunt for food. He had satisfied his hunger earlier by catching a francolin in a small clearing. This chicken-

W.J.Wilwerding

like grouse had given him a good meal, even though he had been robbed of part of it. A jackal had come nosing along as he was nearly finished with his meal. To the jackal fell the head, neck, and feet, a very scant meal indeed in exchange for the smarting scratches he had received on his delicate nose. Flat-eared, swollen-tailed, and spitting, Prowler had bestowed these scratches on the jackal's nose before backing away.

Right now, fully fed and light-headed, Prowler was on the quest of love. Ever it is thus—full of stomach and empty of head. He should have learned better. Burning scratches on face, neck and shoulders still strove to remind him of that same quest the night before which had ended in defeat for him.

Prowler was young; he was sleek, supple, and handsome. One thing he still lacked: he had not as yet learned all the mean villainy practiced by the older tomcats of his clan. This rancorous malignity of the old tom, with a hundred battle experiences behind him, was not yet part of Prowler's nature. In the wilds, love comes only to those who will fight for it with fiendish savagery, giving neither quarter nor advantage to a rival.

Prowler had just grown to full maturity. He lacked battle practice. As yet, he did not have the crusty toughness of an old tom. These take punishment with vindictive bitterness and keep on fighting with savage aggression, though covered with scratches and with ears in tatters.

Prowler was seeking the sleek female bush cat who had come into his life the night before. To be sure, it had been but a brief acquaintance and the lady had not been too friendly. She had spit in his face. Then she had added injury to insult by raking him across the nose with her claws. For a moment, Prowler had forgotten that he was supposed to be a gentleman bush cat. He cuffed her beside the ear. Then she had abandoned any semblance of good breeding to curse him in violent cat language. To this he had replied in kind.

Another Tom, hearing their racket, had come to see what could be done about it. This fellow was thick of head and battle-scarred, with one ear partly missing. He came silent-footed upon the scene. First he disdainfully crouched unseen in the thicket, watching Prowler's attempt at love-making in round-eyed cynical contemplation. Perhaps an idea formed in his sullen, crusty brain that someone who knew how should have a paw in this business. Then he made his explosive ap-

pearance in a wild, scrambling rush that was intended to catch Prowler by surprise and send him scurrying.

But Prowler had a few extra senses in addition to his great sense of patience. He had sensed the presence of his rival. Even as the old tom made his crazy rush at him, Prowler whirled about to meet him. There were a few very clamorous moments of harsh and bitter language, mingled with flashing claws — up, down, left and right.

Now there was a momentary pause for murderous, high, virulent language, while both crouched flat-eared and swollen-tailed. Their maledictions rose to a high wailing and wild shrieks, all run up and mixed together, as if their heinous expressions were being rapidly stirred with a spoon. Then their claws again sought each other's face.

They closed — scratching, slashing, yowling, and screeching! Prowler's sharp claws seared the old tom's nose. Growling horribly, the old rascal reared up to strike back right and left like a boxer. Up and down he struck, with such rapidity and vindictive fury that Prowler seemed to be overwhelmed by a multitude of paws and claws that struck at him from every direction. It appeared as if he might lose all his features under this diabolic onslaught. This was his first battle and too much for his limited experience. Precipitately, he left the field, with the old tom bounding along in his wake. But what Prowler had lacked in fighting experience he made up in fleetness of foot. Rapidly, he left the old tom behind.

But the smarting of his wounds had not stopped Prowler from going on the quest of love again. Perhaps he counted on finding the female alone as he sent out his yowling love call. It was not long before he heard an answering wail at the edge of the thicket below him. He quickened his pace, as he sped toward the sound. To expedite his arrival, he cut straight down through the bushes to the very edge of the grasslands. Here, as he skirted the thicket, he found the going easier in the grass. Having heard no further yowling from the female, he tried to locate her by raising his voice in a high caterwaul. This provided startling results.

A bushbuck, standing at the thicket's edge, barked sharply like a terrier, before bounding away. Prowler stopped with one paw lifted, startled a bit by the bushbuck's sudden bark and departure. Just then, something hissed in his face. This was accompanied by vicious sounds and a savage sweep of five sickle-shaped claws. But the encounter with the bushbuck had cleared Prowler's head to an alert awareness. Even as the leopard hissed *"Phough!"* Prowler had tensed his muscles. He had already bounded to another spot when the leopard's claws cut five furrows in the night air. Prowler had disturbed the spotted one's hunting and the leopard did not like it.

This experience taught Prowler to be more quiet about his prowling. He now went on the hunt for the female in furtive silence. By a roundabout course he made his way toward the place where he had last heard the female bush cat wailing. When he arrived at the spot, he found that his old rival had also heard her cries and had silently gone to the trysting place. No sooner had Prowler arrived than the old tom flew at him in a rage. This time Prowler fought back only briefly before abandoning the field to his rival.

He had no luck with hunting this night, but in the early dawn he saw a dik-dik come furtively from cover to nibble at seed pods growing on thornbushes. Though this was a fully grown antelope with horns, it was only the size of a rabbit. Prowler went into a crouch, patiently waiting for the dik-dik to come close enough for a final rush and spring, but the dik-dik was disposed to feed away from Prowler's hiding place.

With infinite patience and stealth, Prowler stole forward under cover of high grass and bushes. Soft-footed and tense, he crept closer inch by inch. His actions gave the impression of slow motion. When the dik-dik turned its head away, Prowler moved forward. He froze into instant immobility when the little antelope raised its head to look about.

At last, Prowler was almost close enough for a final spring. The dik-dik looked about. Prowler squeezed his form down until he was part of the earth. The dik-dik stared at him, but that motionless form gave no hint of danger. Prowler was hunting upwind, so the dik-dik's sniffing brought no scent of the great peril he was in. Then the dik-dik wandered away, while Prowler patiently crept forward once more. Soon he was again close. Tensing his muscles for a spring, Prowler saw the dik-dik look about, wild-eyed, and then bound for cover.

Prowler, too, looked wildly about to see what had disturbed his hunting. The evidence was plainly at hand. A floating shadow on the ground had caught the dik-dik's eye. Prowler saw this shadow, too, but hesitated for a moment. Then the shadow settled over him and there was a faint whistling sound as the air played a tune in great pinions. Prowler doubled back and sprang for cover, almost turning a backward somersault in his great hurry. A huge wing brushed him, even as he sprang. Great outstretched talons just missed closing on his tail.

From the safety of the dense bushes, Prowler watched as a great crowned hawk-eagle flapped upward on laboring wings to once more take its watch-post on a dead tree that stood alone at the edge of the bush country. Prowler spat in disappointment. The narrow escape was an everyday affair, but he had lost a meal. For a time, he watched the eagle on his perch. He would not forget this eagle, nor the place it used as its accustomed watching-station.

Prowler went up into the big moss-draped forest and, by patient waiting and stalking, managed to catch a grizzled-tan squirrel with a ringed tail. This provided a meal. He attended to his toilet, smoothing his fur with his tongue until he was sleek of appearance. Then he napped.

Some days later, in the early dawn, he picked his way through the bush country, meowing and pricking up his ears for an answer. He had not long to wait. The female bush cat is fickle and ever ready to meow an invitation to any wandering tom cat of her kind, though other toms might be ringed around her in a courting circle. Perhaps she likes to see the toms fighting for her. Whatever the urge, she lured Prowler to her with her siren call — lured him to her and to a contest with another young tom who was waiting in crouched and flat-eared readiness.

Prowler was more experienced in fighting now. Despite his defeats in battle, he was now more sure of himself. So the two fought for the love of a bush cat lady — a vicious, bitter, high-worded duel that observed no rules. Prowler pressed the combat and it was not long before he was all over his opponent, scratching, biting, yowling. The defeated tom fled the battle scene. Prowler chased him for a little distance, then made his confident way back to the female bush cat.

51

His confidence changed when he saw the old demon warrior with the torn ear waiting for him beside the lady cat. Prowler had won her in fair battle and was determined to keep her. However, the first fight had taken something out of him and he was not a match for the old tom. It was not long before he was aware that he must retreat or be torn to bits by the old tom's claws. Once more he turned to run away, but the old tom was possessed by a savage desire to drive his young rival away for good. He stayed close at Prowler's heels, reaching forth now and then to claw at Prowler's tail. So engrossed was he in inflicting punishment that he paid scant attention to where Prowler led him, which was outside of the bush country to the edge of the grasslands. Prowler bounded out into the open, running around the base of a dead tree, as though to put this tree between him and his tormentor.

Whether Prowler did this by design or whether he just happened to run this way is difficult to tell. No one can peer into the recess of a wild creature's mind. Suffice to say that he was very smart and had a very good memory.

Prowler had led the old tom to the dead tree that the crowned hawk-eagle used as a lookout place. The dawn had tinted the snow on Kilimanjaro with morning light and a feathered sentinel was perched in the dead tree.

The mighty-taloned bird looked down with grim and glowering eyes. He dropped as a stone drops into a pool. Perhaps Prowler was listening for the whistle of air through pinions. At any rate, he quickly leaped aside into a thicket. The old tom, surprised at this sudden turn, put on his brakes to change his course. That moment's hesitation sealed his doom. Curved talons cut into him. Screeching and flailing, he was carried aloft. Even before the great bird of prey had reached his perch, the sharp talons had done their work and the wild fire in the old tom's brain had flickered out.

That night there was more yowling and wailing in the bushes that separated the wide grass veld from the forest. This wailing and yowling sounded very much like a backyard serenade in our more civilized land. Prowler was courting and thus it is that African bush cats give utterance to their affections.

7: Tiny of the Thornbush

It was sunset time in Tanganyika, East Africa, as Tiny, the little dik-dik antelope, followed his mother and father along a dusty game trail that was hedged high by thornbushes. He was only ten inches high, but he was built like a dainty deer fawn. His parents were of about the size and color of a gray rabbit. Tiny's hornless mother was but sixteen inches high at the shoulder, just an inch taller than her mate, who had small, black, pointed horns. A sort of proboscis gave their noses a strange appearance.

As dusk descended on the wild Pare Mountain jungle of thorny trees and bushes, a hyena wailed like a fire siren, jackals yapped, and doves cooed in their roosts in the weru-weru trees. Tiny was just a few days old. The jungle sounds made him crowd close to his mother. He still nursed and was not interested in the beanlike pods of the thornbushes, on which his parents fed.

53

Tiny's father suddenly stopped his browsing to whistle sharply, like the shrill chirp of a bird. At once, all three dik-dik bounded high, as if propelled on springs. Away they went in quick bounds and into the thick cover of the thornbush. The old dik-dik had caught the evil reek of a big bat-eared spotted hyena, as this beast came clumping along the trail. Soon after he passed, the little dik-dik quickly got over their alarm and resumed their feeding.

They lived in the western foothills of the Pare Mountains, which was also the boulder-strewn and thorn-grown home of the rhinoceros. The small dik-dik and the big rhinoceros often browsed on the leaves and blossoms of the same kinds of wild shrubs. These two kinds of animals are often found in the same districts in Africa. Except to avoid being stepped on by the big beast, the dik-dik paid no attention to the rhinoceros. Quite frequently, they walked close to him as he fed.

One day, at dawn, the old pair took Tiny down a game path that was much used by the rhinoceros in going to his bedroom in the thorn-bushes near the top of the ravine. The trail wound among huge rocks, midst acacia and euphorbia trees, as it followed the edge of the ravine. This shaded ravine stank of leopards who had their lairs in the rocky walls. The little dik-dik took a branch trail away from the leopard stench. Very soon they knew that a leopard was returning to his den after a late meal in early morning.

The leopard had eaten just before the dawn. Since there was now no reason why he should walk in stealth, he walked boldly along a game trail. It was therefore easy for the dik-dik to keep track of the leopard's movements by just listening to the sounds of this thorny jungle.

From thickets of acacia and euphorbia to the north, there came the bleating goatlike cry of the "go-way" birds — long-tailed black and white touracos. A bit closer, a black-headed yellow oriole cried like a cat as it saw the leopard pass. A few minutes later there was the throat-clearing sound that the rabbit-size hyrax makes, *"Who-whack-chuck!"* The leopard would now be among the huge granite rocks on which the gray-furred hyrax sat in rows. Now, suddenly, there was a bedlam of barking, grunting and chattering, as the baboons and guenon monkeys discovered the leopard and raised a wild alarm.

The monkeys followed the leopard for a time, making an infernal racket as they jumped from tree to tree and bushtop to bushtop. In

their own tongue they seemed to cry, *"Robber, scoundrel, murderer!"*
The whole wild jungle world took up the alarm, as crows, white-necked
ravens, and smaller birds of every color added their voices to those of
the rabble of monkeys. Then, for a bit, there was quiet. The leopard
had no doubt eluded his hostile followers by taking to the thorn thickets, threading his way underneath the spiked branches where none
could watch his going. Now the old dik-dik pair took a trail leading
downhill, apparently aware that the leopard would follow an uphill
trail to his den. They had listened their way to safety. As they daintily
stepped along, they heard the sharp bark of a bushbuck from back near
the ravine and they knew that the leopard was near his lair.

Early morning and evening were the dik-dik's chief times for feeding.
This also is the time when clawed and fanged hunters are apt to be
abroad. One evening, as the old pair were browsing, with Tiny standing close by, the leopard came early from his lair. Just once did he
voice his call, *"Uh-har-r, uh-har-r!"* It sounded exactly like a saw having hard going through a log. Then he was quiet, for it was not usual
for him to advertise where he was going. He was now a wraith in the
thorny jungle, stalking without sound on velvet-padded paws. He was
hidden in the evening's shadows. Birds and monkeys had already gone
to roost and there were none to call warnings to the little dik-dik. The
leopard now followed the same game trail where they browsed on shoots.

With indescribable stealth, the leopard approached the little dik-dik
as they fed. He was gathering his hindquarters for a spring, when
Tiny's father shrilly whistled in alarm. A faint breeze had betrayed the
leopard, for his cat stink went with him. He sprang, but the dik-dik
went aloft on the natural springs in their legs. In one fleet second the
leopard was leaping at them and, in the next second, they were gone.
Furious at having missed his prey, the leopard sulked for a time in the
dust of the trail before seeking other prey.

As the weeks passed, Tiny learned much about his jungle home. He
soon found out that many birds are harmless and would warn him of
approaching danger. But he also learned that some very large birds
came nose-diving to earth to pounce on little jungle folk. He had so
far avoided these because his parents scurried for thorn cover when a
shadow suddenly appeared over them.

A day came when Tiny heard his father's sharp whistle. Tiny and his mother quickly darted for the cover of thorn bushes. Just as they did this, a big tawny eagle swooped down. From this day, Tiny never again saw his father. He and his mother followed the trails by themselves. At first, his mother stopped every now and then to look about, as if expecting her mate to come along. After a time, she seemed to know that the one she looked for would never be at her side again.

The weeks grew into months and Tiny became full-grown. Now, he had little pointed horns. He was about fifteen inches high at the shoulder, as big as he would grow. His mother was no longer with him. One night the leopard had come along the trail. Tiny had smelled the big cat and had bounded away. But from this time on he had never again seen his mother.

On an early dew-drenched and blossom-scented morning, Tiny was leisurely following a game trail. Most night beasts had already gone to their lairs. Tiny was busy feeding on the tender shoots of the bushes that hedged the trail. Soon, he heard harsh barking as the baboons were on their way into the hills.

There was a large rowdy crowd of baboons in this troop. Old, grizzled-gray dog baboons led the troop. These were the advance warriors that acted as guards. They were followed by females and young of all sizes. The very young ones clung to their mothers' breasts, while those a bit older rode jockeylike on their mothers' backs, holding on by clutching handfuls of fur. At the rear of this troop came another guard of tough old males. Many of these big fellows were as large as a retriever dog and had fangs rivaling those of the leopard in size.

The baboons ate anything that was eatable. They even ate scorpions by quickly pulling the stinger from the tail and popping the unarmed scorpion into the mouth. One big baboon could readily tear Tiny limb from limb and feed on his tender flesh. Tiny had learned that these fellows were rough and dangerous. Nervously, he moved along the trail to avoid them.

Tiny's attention was concentrated on the sounds made by the advancing baboons, and he failed to see what was in the trail before him. A brown-mottled, greenish-gray thing lay coiled in the dust of the trail. It was a rock python, mean in every inch of its length. Quickly, it struck at Tiny, fastening its curved teeth into one of his legs. Whistling in shrill alarm, Tiny tried to struggle free.

W.J.Wilwerding

This was not a huge python as pythons grow, but it was long enough and strong enough to overcome Tiny. Despite his frantic struggles, he could not free himself of the python's hold. It slithered its muscular length through the dust to throw a coil over Tiny. Once this was accomplished, the little dik-dik would be doomed.

An old male baboon who led the troop was attracted by Tiny's struggles and hurried forward to catch him. But now, as he was close, he saw the python in the trail between him and his expected prey. For a moment he hesitated and then he saw that the python had hold of the dik-dik.

Baboons very readily lose their tempers. This one, thinking that the python had come to steal his prey, blew up like a charge of dynamite. Going into a rage, he grasped the python's muscular body with his hairy hands. Savagely, he bit into it. African rock pythons also have evil tempers. This one released its hold on Tiny to swiftly dart about. It fastened its teeth in the baboon's shoulder. Holding the python's body tightly in both black hands, the baboon sank his long fangs deeply into the snake's stout muscles. At the same time, he pushed the snake away from him, tearing a great gash in the python. He repeated this biting and pushing until the big snake was bitten almost in two. A hard pull with both hairy hands and he held the python in two parts.

During this struggle, there had been a terrific bedlam of hoarse grunting and barking, as the entire baboon troop had come up to watch the fray. Tiny had bounded away as soon as the python had released its hold on him. He listened to the sounds of combat from a distance.

For some time, the baboon warriors worried what remained of the snake. Then they feasted on its meat. Gradually, the excited barking ceased and there was just contented grunting. So Tiny knew that the battle and the danger were over. He was sore where the python had bitten him in the leg, but a python's fangs are not poisonous and he would soon recover.

A few days later, Tiny had entirely forgotten about his encounter with the python. He was walking along a game trail when a female dik-dik walked close. He touched noses with her. Then the two walked side by side, browsing on the bushes the way Tiny often had done with his mother. During the worst heat of the day, the two spent the hours in a shaded retreat. At dusk, when the members of the dik-dik clan like to fare forth, Tiny set out with his mate.

The beasts of the night were already preparing to go hunting and there was grunting, howling and roaring. From afar, on the lower veld, came the high barking of the zebras. Tiny paid scant attention to these calls of the evening, except to note that the calls of the meat eaters were not too close. There were again two sets of ears, eyes, and noses to listen, watch, and smell for danger. Tiny's lonely days on the thorn-hedged trails were over.

8: The Dancers in the Trees

Reza, the colobus monkey, was born in the high forest trees of the big mountain where the long gray mosses bearded the branches. Organ shrikes fluted, and red-breasted trogans flitted through the shaded greenery of the forest roof. Reza was completely dressed in white in his baby clothes, like the other very young colobus babies that the monkey mothers clutched tightly to their breasts. Reza was cuddled in his mother's arms, while many of the colobus monkey troop were engaged in what looked very much like a dance. The grown monkeys were all dressed in black and white. Their brown eyes peered from black faces ringed with white. From their shoulders long silky white mantles of fur draped gracefully to meet the long white hairs of their tails. These long white hairs waved with the rhythm of their leaping up and down on branches, while they crooned, *"Roo-roo-roo-roo!"*

It looked as if the monkeys were celebrating the birth of little Reza, but they always went into this song and dance business near sunrise time. It may have been their way of showing happiness that a new day had begun. At times, they also danced this way before bedtime.

They grasped the branches with four-fingered hands, because, unlike most monkeys, they had no thumbs. They were big monkeys, the old males being almost as large as a baboon. Their fur grew thickly, because here on the side of the big mountain the nights were often cold.

Now they stopped their jumping about and began hunting their breakfast of tender leaves and buds. They were happy when they found seeds and fruit. This part of the big forest had been selected by this troop of colobus monkeys as their home. Though usually gentle and peace-loving, the old males had powerful jaws and stout, long canine teeth that were sharp weapons. They allowed no other colobus monkey troops to invade the privacy of this section of the forest, which they had selected as their own particular home ground. Always restless and moving from one part of their forest home to another, they made tremendous leaps from branch to branch. They had regular paths, or roads, through the treetops — trees and branches that they were accustomed to using day after day as the best ways to go from one place to another.

When he was older, Reza rode on his mother's back. He liked to perch on her shoulder when she sat feeding on leaves. He was now dressed in black and white like his mother. Nature usually gives this skunklike attire of black and white to animals that make big stinks, but the colobus monkeys were an exception. They were clean, with the sweet, woodsy scent of the forest in their fur.

Doves everlastingly cooed, "*Coo-coo-cucu-cucu.*" Bush robins sang. Little white-eyes, which looked like small warblers with white-rimmed glasses, flitted about. Chameleons moved slowly about on lichen-covered trunks and branches of trees, so closely imitating the bark with their colors that even the sharp-eyed monkeys had to look twice to see that living creatures clung there. Blue monkeys barked like squirrels and, very strangely, the colobus monkeys made no attempt to drive them from this part of the forest. Here there was plenty of food for leaf-eaters like the colobus monkeys.

There was a spring in the forest where the monkeys could go to drink. The colobus were rarely found far from water. Though essentially tree-dwellers, they did come down to run across the forest floor and then they had to be unusually wary and alert. Leopards lived down here, as did other wild cats, and now and then a spitting cobra might rear up and spit venom in one's eyes.

Like a little jockey in a black and white costume, Reza rode on his mother's back when she scampered across the forest floor to go to drink at the spring. This late afternoon there were elephants there, throwing water over themselves and making a rather muddy mess of things about the spring. The elephants did not mind having the colobus monkeys scampering about near them. The monkeys drank from little pools that had formed where the elephants had made deep imprints in the soft earth with their big feet. Reza was accustomed to seeing the big, gray elephants with their shining ivory tusks. He already knew that elephants did not harm monkeys or the birds that came to drink and that often perched on the elephants' heads.

A big black forest hog, an ugly beast with long wartlike growths on the sides of his head, came down to drink. The monkeys scampered to one side at this one's approach. Old boar forest hogs could not be trusted. They might even try to attack and eat a monkey, for they often were predatory. Even the elephants warily watched this beast. Old cows reached forth with their trunks to chase their young calves beneath their big bodies. They could have picked up this big hog and tossed him aside, but they knew he might have done some vicious cutting with his tusks in the meantime. They let him drink at the opposite edge of the pool, but when he attempted to get into the mud and wallow with the elephants, a big bull almost blasted him off his feet with a squirt of water from his trunk. The hog angrily gnashed his tusks together and scampered aside as the elephant lowered his tusks as if to impale him.

Reza watched all this from a perch in a nearby tree where his mother had taken him as soon as the big black hog had appeared. Reza was busy chewing on a tender leaf, as he was now learning to pluck food for himself. He really had no fear of that big hog. Having had no experiences with forest hogs, he did not as yet know that, though some great beasts could be trusted, others not so big could not be trusted. The only way that he learned about other animals that lived here was by the attitudes of his mother and the other monkeys. When they ran to avoid some animal, he knew by instinct that this beast should be avoided. In the same way, he learned by watching the older monkeys that one could scamper right around the feet of the elephants without coming to harm.

The broad, well-beaten paths of the elephants led everywhere through this forest and the monkeys often used these as roads when they went to the ground and ran from one big tree to another. One wondered why they went to the ground when they were far safer in the trees above, but they were everlastingly active and on the move. When some of the troop went down to earth, all the rest followed with their long white plumes of hair waving at every jump.

They moved along in a black and white line as if they were playing follow-the-leader. In places where storms had knocked down trees, everything was a tangle of branches covered with hanging beards of gray moss. This hanging moss looked much like the waving long hairs of the monkeys' white mantles. It served to hide them from prying eyes when they sat in the branches with the moss hanging all around them.

But there were prying eyes from above the forest trees that readily saw the colobus monkeys. This was especially so when Reza's mother went with the rest of the troop to the topmost branches to feed on the tender shoots that grew there. Now the tops of the big trees were dotted with the black and white monkeys and one could see them from afar. The moss and the forest's shadows no longer hid them from view.

Reza picked at tender shoots and leaves, testing these to see if one was better than the other. His mother perched on a limb next to Reza's father, the big leader of this troop, very serious of face and with a high black pompadour of hair sitting like a thick fur cap on the top of his head. The pair were busily stuffing themselves with this tender leaf salad when a floating shadow passed over the treetops as if cast by something that soared overhead.

There were many creatures soaring above the forest in this place: hawks, vultures, and eagles, all of whom lived on meat. The vultures lived mainly on meat left by the lion and leopard. Others of the feathered world did their own hunting, and no creature of a size to be their prey was safe from their beaks and talons.

Right now, had the colobus monkeys been on their guard instead of being so busy with their eating, they would have seen that the one who soared overhead was a crowned hawk-eagle. This very large, crested eagle was both powerful and exceedingly fierce. The great forest eagle was out hunting, and his favorite food was monkeys. Now

his sharp eyes were searching the upper branches for his prey. Often, when this feathered disaster was just soaring about and enjoying himself, he called in a shrill, musical manner, but he uttered no sound now that he was hunting.

As the eagle's shadow passed over the green crowns of the big trees, some blue, or Sykes', monkeys saw him and barked like squirrels. The colobus monkeys knew this alarm call of the blue monkeys and at once all were alert. Most of them scampered to lower branches to get under the protection of a heavy cover of leaves. Reza's father, being the leader of the troop, looked inquiringly about to see where the danger was coming from.

The eagle had seen the old male monkey perched there with his mate and young one. The huge bird of prey folded his wings and fell as though weighted with lead. Fierce-eyed and with talons spread, he dropped into the tree near where Reza was clinging to his mother's back as she hurriedly scurried for cover. Reza's father was hurrying along the branch behind them. He turned to look up and the great bird set its talons in him just below the shoulders. Reza felt the brush of powerful wings as the eagle spread his great pinions to break his fall.

Up, up, over the treetops on heavily laboring wings, the big eagle lifted his heavy monkey prey. But Reza's father had managed to twist about and grasp the eagle's neck with his black hands. He pulled the fierce head to him and set his stout, sharp cutting teeth into the eagle's throat. He put his powerful jaw muscles into the bite and bit until the clutching talons grew weak in their hold. With great sweeps, the wings beat and beat and then, over and over they went and down, down in a great turning and twisting and feeble flailing of wings until they fell into the trees. Now the eagle's talons had released their hold and the great bird of prey was dead.

Fortunately for Reza's father, they fell into a heavily leafed treetop that acted like a net. The big monkey grabbed at leaves and branches as he fell and broke his fall. The big eagle hung limply from a limb for a moment and then overbalanced to plunge through the branches to earth. Down there, where only little spots of sunlight found their way through to dapple the forest floor with gold, the big black forest hog devoured the eagle.

Above, in the shaded greenery of the big mavuli tree, Reza's father licked his grievous wounds. It would take time for these to heal, for he was badly pierced by the talons, but his thick fur had given him some protection and saved him from mortal injury. He was healthy and strong and would soon be whole again.

Reza had learned about eagles. The colobus monkeys had all had a great fright. These attacks occurred every now and then when they went to feed in the top branches where the tender shoots were so good and sweet. It was not long before they were back at their feeding. Reza was again busy with plucking his green food. One monkey began a dance, jumping up and down on a branch with his long white mantle and tail gracefully waving to his movements. Others joined him to jump up and down on the branches, while they crooned, *"Roo-roo-roo!"*

You can hear the colobus monkeys crooning on that mountainside in northern Tanganyika on any nice day, especially in the morning or in the evening. During the cold nights, they huddle close for warmth, but in the clear, warm days, they feed and dance and are happy. With the good care of his mother, Reza no doubt lived to be a big, handsome mountain colobus monkey. That may be he who is calling *"Roo-roo-roo,"* while he dances the dance of the colobus as the African tribesmen call it, up there on the mighty mountainside of Kilimanjaro, with its snow-topped crown gleaming in the equatorial sun.

6:
The Way
of the
Wary

It had rained before the dawn, scenting the African morning air with a fresh, earthy smell, mingled with the perfume of jasmine and flowering aloes. A black-headed yellow oriole called, *"Two-uh-lit,"* and blended this with the liquid, slurring whistle of his cheery song. His mate, who looked exactly like him in dress, had just left her cuplike nest of grass hung beneath the branch-tip of an acacia. She mewed like a cat in answer to her mate's call. Two green bee-eaters with cinnamon vests perched on a coral-colored blossom branch of an aloe and squeaked, *"Tee-si-ip, tsee-ip."* Rocky, the hyrax, had his inquisitive nose thrust out of a rock crevice, warily looking and listening to see if it was safe to venture forth. Apparently assured that all was well, for otherwise the birds would have been excitedly chattering instead of singing, he scrambled up the big, rounded granite boulder that was the bastion of his rocky fortress.

Rocky was a rock hyrax, called "rock rabbit" by some, though he was not even closely related to a rabbit. He did look much like a gray rabbit with very short ears, but a glance at his feet would have convinced any doubter that here was a strange beast that certainly was no rabbit. His toes had black, rounded, hooflike nails, except on the hind inner toes, where they were more like claws. If he had a tail, it was so short that you did not see it. The moist, rubbery soles of his feet could be drawn up into cones that acted like suction cups. The hyrax can climb up the almost vertical face of a rock with these efficient suction-cup feet.

Rocky cleared his throat and gave the "all-clear" call. The "all-clear" call sounded as if he was clearing his throat and was preparing to spit — it had that spitting quality to it. One by one, his mate and four young popped their heads up. Soon they all were squatting in a furry row on top of the big gray rock, with their bright eyes surveying the rocky and thorny scene that was their domain.

Shortly, there were other family groups of hyrax squatting in rows on other rocks nearby. While many eyes watched the beasts and birds that walked and flew about on this rocky slope of the Pare Mountains in northern Tanganyika, there was considerable conversation among the hyrax families. The hyraxes called back and forth in their hissing, throat-clearing manner, "*Hoo-wack-kuk*" and, "*Wack-kak-ick*," or "*Woo-kick-ook*." Anyone's guess is as good as another's as to what the hyraxes meant by these sounds. Apparently the sounds communicated warnings and other meanings. At the "all-clear" call, all noses popped up and hyraxes came forth from hiding. When one or more hissed the danger call, the rocks were cleared of hyraxes as if by magic. One moment, little gray-brown furry fellows were perched everywhere. The next moment, there were only the bare rocks splashed with white from the hyraxes' droppings, as if someone had thrown whitewash at the rocks.

It was time to get something to eat. The hyraxes were strict vegetarians. Rocky and his family ran down the rocks when the "all-clear" was given. They followed well-beaten paths through the grass that ran from big rock to big rock. Here they hunted for green shoots of grass, fresh green leaves, and blossoming flowers. Always there were hyrax sentinels perched somewhere on the high rocks to give the alarm call if danger approached.

The danger that came near this morning did not come afoot, but out of the sky. Two martial eagles were perched high on a big rock that reared up out of the mountainside, above the place where the hyrax colony lived. The big crested eagles had a growing young one to feed in their nest and had waited until there was activity in the hyrax colony below. Their telescopic eyes told them when the hyraxes were at their morning feeding. Down came the eagles out of the morning sky — twin brown-feathered bombs. Spitting alarm calls of hyrax sentinels hissed from rock to rock. One eagle missed his quarry, as the

hyrax scurried into a rock cleft; the other made his strike. As Rocky and his family darted for cover, a neighboring hyrax was lifted aloft and carried away to the eagles' aerie. This hyrax had hesitated a moment too long over a bit of juicy new grass.

It took a bit of time for the hyrax colony to get over its fright. After a while, when all seemed calm outside, one nose poked forth and was followed by the owner thereof. Now Rocky sat warily on a rock to keenly look about. He gave the "all-clear" signal and soon others popped their heads up. Now, one after another popped out of their hiding places and once again the rocks were lined with furry forms. Now there were other "all-clear" signals all along the mountainside. Once more the hyraxes scurried along their paths from rock to rock. An alarm is sounded in the wild; someone loses a race with fate; but life must go on and so the danger and the recent tragedy seem to be forgotten. But perhaps they are never forgotten and the little creatures always keep these things in their memories.

Anyway, the hyraxes were feeding again and they were as wary as ever. Sentinels watched; everyone was ready to run for cover at the first hint of danger or the first alarm note.

Rocky fed beside his mate, surrounded by their four young. He looked about and apparently saw something slithering in the grass. Peering sharply in that direction, he saw nothing moving just then. Now he angrily stamped one foot the way a rabbit thumps. This brought results. Snakes are not supposed to be able to hear sounds, but to feel vibrations. This one, which happened to be a rock python, must have felt the vibrations of that stamping foot. Its head darted forward. It was not a very large python, perhaps about seven feet long, but it could have easily made a meal of a young hyrax. Apparently, a hyrax was what it was hunting for among these rocks. It could hardly have made a meal of Rocky, but it had the strength in its constricting muscles to crush him until he was dead.

Rocky had sharp chisel-like cutting teeth in the front of his mouth. He knew how to use these teeth and did use them in fighting. Though he was often wary to the point of timidity, he was no coward and he could give a good account of himself in a fight with his own kind or with any other creature of his size. But this slithering snake was something that he did not quite understand. Maybe he sensed that its enveloping coils were something that he could not cope with. At any rate, as it slid toward him, he gave the alarm call. The hyraxes were feeding in a path right beside a huge rock. They went up its almost vertical side as if an elevator had whisked them up.

Now the hyraxes squatted on top of the rock to watch a hunting party of a dozen big, banded mongooses surround the reptile. They had soon cut it up and served it in the best mongoose style. Their meat often came by the yard instead of by the pound and they polished it off foot by foot under the bright African sun. This was one menace less in the hyraxes' front yard.

Rocky did not mind having the mongooses about. They disposed of snakes that might give him trouble. He also did not mind the black-faced guenon monkeys that often came here to hunt for roots and insects among the big rocks. These green-gray long-tailed monkeys were almost as agile as the hyraxes in climbing about on the rocks. Baboons also came here to grub for food. One could see where they had been digging for roots and grubs around clumps of grass and scrub bushes of thorn. With these fellows, Rocky never took risks. The grown male baboons were big rough fellows. One would not want to get close to their

clutching black fingers and long fangs. Rocky and his friends usually sat on the tops of the high rocks when the baboons were about, watching the baboons and haranguing them with uncomplimentary spitting remarks. When the baboons came close or ran up on the rocks, all the hyraxes ran for cover.

One morning, when Rocky was watching the baboons, he saw a leopard sneaking close to the dog-faced monkeys. Rocky sounded the alarm, because the leopard also was his enemy. The baboons knew the alarm call of the hyrax. Now the baboon sentinels, who had not as yet seen the leopard, barked their sharp danger calls. But the warning came too late for one baboon. At the first warning call, the leopard sprang. He was already making off with his prey in his jaws.

At their fellow's harsh cry of despair, the other big baboons rallied to his defense. There was a savage battle that continued loudly for a long way through high grass, thornbushes, rocks and groves of barbed euphorbia trees. Eventually, the furious racket of the encounter died away in the distance and Rocky could not see who had won the fight.

The baboons and leopard having gone, everything seemed safe, so Rocky sounded the "all-clear." Down off the big, gray, lichen-covered rock, the whole family came scurrying. Then they were happily running along their grass trails, having a picnic lunch of everything green they could find. They were so busy with this that, for once, someone forgot to give the danger call when a serval cat, big as a bobcat, sneaked close.

This long-legged, spotted wild cat had been crouching quietly in nearby bushes all the time that the leopard had stalked the baboon and while the big fight was on. He, too, had hoped to catch a baboon, but not being as big as a leopard he had to be more cautious about his hunting of baboons. Also, he had seen the leopard and was not disposed to dispute hunting rights with the larger cat. So, with the great patience of all the cats, the serval had waited. Now he saw the hyraxes coming down off the rocks to feed. He had missed getting a baboon, but a hyrax would do, so he waited in ambush for one to come close.

Rocky was scampering along the grassy path toward a bush that had fresh green shoots. This path took him directly toward the waiting serval. The light grayish tan of the cat, broken up with its dark spots, concealed him perfectly. All he had to do was wait until Rocky was close enough for just one jump with outstretched claws. This serval

could run down his prey, but he knew that hyraxes did their running on the tops of rocks.

The bush toward which Rocky ran was right beside one of the huge rocks. The hyraxes were forever careful that their feeding paths were close to big rocks. In a low branch of a tree above the bush where the serval crouched, a white-bellied go-way bird alighted. It was about the size of a large grackle. Raising the long crest on its head and cocking up its long tail, as if trying to keep from losing its balance, the bird looked down. Despite the concealing quality of the serval's colors, the bird's sharp eyes saw him. At once, the gray, white, and black bird bleated like a goat, "*Ba-haa!*" It broke like a trumpet call into the morning sounds. The serval knew what this call meant and so did Rocky. Everyone who lived in this bush and rock country knew the alarm call of the go-way bird. The serval tensed his muscles and sprang. In that split second, Rocky sprang to the big rock. Up he went like a furred streak, running up the almost vertical face of the rock as if he were on level ground. His mate and family had scampered up other rocks and all were safe in cracks that afforded places of refuge. The serval wrinkled his nose and snarled, and what he said to the go-way bird is not fit to mention.

It was not long before Rocky's young ones had become independent of the old ones. They went their various ways to form family groups of their own in other rocky places. Now, Rocky and his mate had three new young ones hidden like mice in the grass- and fur-lined nest, safe in a rocky cleft. Unlike newly born mice, these young hyraxes had their eyes open and were fully clothed in fur.

As soon as the young hyraxes were about the size of a grown rat and clothed in soft, brown, downy fur, they chased each other about on the rocks, playing like kittens. Rocky and his mate watched over them, ever alert for their welfare. In the wilds, it is the wary and watchful who survive. Rocky knew this. He had learned caution from the day when he had first left the home nest to climb upon a rock and look about.

A shadow passed over the rocks where the hyraxes sat in a long family row. A martial eagle soared above them. Rocky hissed the alarm call, "*Who-whack-chuck!*" As if a magician had waved his wand, little bundles of brown fur vanished from sight. Except for those white splashes on the immense gray granite rocks, one never would have known that cute little furry creatures lived here. This is the way of the wary hyrax and the ways of the wary are ever mysterious. No doubt Rocky was teaching his young to be everlastingly aware of danger, but, who knows what wild creatures think about?

10: Creeping Vengeance

It was a beautiful moonlit night in Africa, a place of seeming peace, where night birds and little brown-furred galagos called and played in the moon's mystic light. But, in the stretch of dense bush that grew between the big forest and grass veld, there was hissing, growling, and low, beastly sounds. Murder had been done in the dark shadows. Even now, the killers were disposing of the victim's remains by eating him. A gang of hyenas had come upon a sick impala lying in the bushes and had forever cured him of his illness.

A big mongoose came through the bush country in his undulating fashion, which resembled the movements of a playing porpoise. Raising his grizzled and banded form stiffly erect on the tips of his hind feet and tail, as if held up on a tripod, the mongoose moved his triangular head viperlike from side to side. He sniffed and sniffed, hissed through set teeth, and, dropping on his short legs once more, went away from this place of death.

One of the largest of the mongoose clan, almost as big as a fair-sized otter, Bandy the banded mongoose resembled his cousins from India in general form, but his body was marked with a series of dark bands. His kind are found in Africa, from the Cape of Good Hope to Abyssinia. At times they hunt in troops of a dozen or more, but Bandy hunted alone.

Bandy grumbled and mumbled to himself as he went along, his mind afire with the scene he just had witnessed. Something with outstretched claws pounced at him. He executed a side-flip underneath thorn branches, hissing in exasperation. What a place this was to live and hunt in. One could not venture out of one's burrow on a respectable hunt for food without running into gibbering, cackling, and evil-smelling murderers, or being pounced at by silent-footed ones who waited evilly beside the trails. Something should really be done about this. Something was done right then and there.

The serval cat who had pounced at Bandy was questing about to see where his intended victim had gone, when an African black cobra, rising swiftly from the earth with a graceful, sweeping motion, struck at the spotted cat like a thing electrified. The serval yowled in terror and struck back with unsheathed claws. The cobra struck again. Feebly, the cat struck back, then, tottering giddily, it crawled off into the shadows to die.

Bandy should have blessed the cobra for having so easily and quickly removed one of his enemies. But if Bandy had blessed a cobra with anything but his sharp teeth, he would not have been a big brave mongoose. Meat does not come by the yard every day. At once, the serval cat was forgotten in the red fever of the hunt. The cobra saw Bandy's stealthy approach; its evil head swayed like a raised pendulum in the moonlight. Like the swiftly moving shadow of a passing bird, the deadly head darted forward and down — but Bandy was not there when it struck.

Again and again the cobra raised its head to strike at this creature that crouched before it with arched back. It was just as if it struck at nothing, for always Bandy contrived to be some other place when that deadly head came down.

After a time the cobra began to tire; its strikes were neither as swift nor as frequent. Once more Bandy moved in. The cobra struck. Deftly, Bandy moved just far enough aside to avoid the strike. In one fleet move, he had the cobra's head in his mouth. There was a lashing, curling, convulsive twisting of six feet of scaled length. There was a crunching sound of teeth; and the battle was over. Bandy dragged the limp form, its tail still wiggling, into the thornbushes and prepared to literally feed at length.

A big black muzzle, armed with a formidable array of teeth, poked into the thornbushes with a horrid cackling laugh. This beast towered over Bandy as an elephant towers over a pygmy, but Bandy was reckless with fury and bit this beast in the nose. There was a throaty growl and a murderous chop of teeth. Bandy had leaped to one side before those teeth closed on him. Now the bat-eared robber of a hyena dragged the cobra's length out of the bushes and undertook to devour it.

Bandy flamed into anger. He rushed from spot to spot, circling about and jumping up on a log to better view this outrageous act. He hissed, he whistled; the hair upon his body stood out and his tail was swollen like that of a cat with its back up. He raised himself up on his hind legs to emit another shrill whistle. It was all to no avail. The hyena had no respect for the rights of any other beast on earth. Soon there was nothing left to rave or complain about. Other hyenas, having finished their evil business in the thornbushes, were coming this way attracted by the scent of the dead serval cat. Bandy prudently left the scene.

As he went mumbling along a trail, Bandy met a jackal coming to the scent of meat. The jackal snapped at him, but Bandy now had enough of this business of being snapped at. He buried his teeth in the jackal's nose and held on. There followed a wild run through high grass, the jackal yelping at every jump. Bandy doggedly hung onto the jackal's nose, swinging there like a rag doll. Finally, crazed with the pain in his nose, the jackal turned into the thornbush. The raking thorns made

77

W.J.Wilwerding

the game a bit rough for Bandy and he let go of his hold, leaving the jackal to yap his wild way into the moonlit haze.

Whereupon, finding himself free for the time from swaggering rascals, Bandy pursued his hunting. A veld rat crossed his path, and fortunately for Bandy, and not for the rat, he caught it and fed. He later had a few mouse-sized gerbilles for dessert. These look much like diminutive kangaroo rats. Bandy now directed his course toward the home burrow — a deserted termite mound in whose underground corridors he made his home. Here he curled up in sleep.

The early hours of the next evening found Bandy hungry again and eager for the hunt. The lurking dangers of other nights had taught him caution. Coming furtively to the burrow's entrance, he first stuck his head out to quest about with his nose and beady eyes before venturing forth.

Bandy's way took him to the edge of the bush country, where, in high grass, a francolin covered a nest of eggs. The chickenlike francolin took to wings at his approach, but the eggs offered a tempting treat. Biting a hole in one, he began sucking at its contents, but soon the heavy padding of feet caused him to sit stiffly erect. His visitor was not long in arriving. The slouching manner and bat ears clearly identified the hyena. Again, Bandy had to surrender his meal.

Bandy had just a taste of the egg, and now eggs, nice warm eggs, kept chasing each other around in his fiery brain. He went along a trail that took him to a *shamba*, or small African farm, at the edge of the bush country. Here stood the round mud and wattle huts of the Africans. It was dark now and the people had retired to their huts for the night. Eggs were in Bandy's mind, the taste of one was in his mouth, and eggs he must have. He knew very well where he could get them. He had been egg hunting in this same village before. Without any trouble, he now found where the poultry was kept. His nose brought to him the warm, stuffy smell of roosting fowl.

The people who live in the African wilds know very well that many kinds of night-hunting creatures also inhabit this land of theirs. The hut in which the poultry was kept was well protected. Bandy sniffed about at every crack or possible opening, but no entrance presented itself. Finally, he found a place where a rat had burrowed under the hut. Industriously, he went to work to enlarge the burrow. This took considerable digging, which he did not particularly care about, but the thought of the taste of eggs kept him at it.

At last, Bandy had an opening large enough to admit him. He found eggs in the nests which the Africans had failed to gather. Eggs could be gathered at any time that one wanted them, so the Africans did not habitually gather them every day. Bandy ate eggs until he was full and then, for a time, he curled up in a nest and slept.

He may have slept for about an hour when he heard scratching sounds near the place where he had burrowed his way into the hut. He raised his minklike head to sniff and listen. Then he scampered to the hole to make his exit. As soon as he poked his nose out of the hole he knew who had been scratching there. The rascally hyena was trying to get in at the hens. Bandy watched his chance. When the hyena went prowling around on the other side of the hut, he emerged to scuttle across the compound. A slouching, bat-eared form came at him from the shadows. Just as Bandy was darting under some thornbushes, snapping fangs made a great chopping sound within an inch of his back. But, in the wilds of Africa, as in other places, misses do not count.

Bandy went on his way, thinking himself free of the hyena's unwelcome company. Soon he heard the heavy clumping of following feet. The hyena was on his trail. Bandy kept on, stopping neither to look nor to sniff. In and out among bushes and rocks he threaded his way, searching low spots near a marsh and stream. He seemed to be hunting for something that was not easy to find. On and on he went, with those heavy footfalls always coming closer. At last, near dawn, with the baboons already calling in their hollow, booming manner, he came upon the thing that he was seeking. Perhaps this was by intent, but it might be that he found it by pure chance — who can know or tell?

In a stony bit of ground he found it — a thing of sinister design; perhaps there are some who might have thought it beautiful. If color and pattern alone give beauty to a creature, then this one could have been called beautiful. Cerulean blue it was, as well as cobalt, purple, olive, yellow, and black. The colors were in a pattern, blended and shaded into a magnificent ensemble and design, as if some master craftsman had woven them thus on a loom. But the creature that wore this colorful garb was really a thing of horror to look upon. It was a short, fat, ugly, and frightful thing. Its flat, triangular head was set with two pale, lidless, slit-pupiled eyes. Its blunt nose was arrayed with a number of spikes or horns. Men had first looked upon this horned-nosed creature and called it the "rhinoceros viper." Having fashioned this super-venomous thing, Nature must have relented and colored it with many hues to warn all living things against it.

Fast as chain lightning was the strike of this viper, but it was otherwise slow of movement. Its neck was bent into an S; its malevolent head was poised for action above its thick form. Thus it waited for any creature that might venture near.

Bandy knew the nature of this creature. Warily he circled it, one eye on it and the other watching for the hyena who was following him. In other circumstances, Bandy would have killed the reptile and eaten it. Now he did not move in close enough to draw its strike. He circled just far enough away to keep it coiled and ready to strike. Now the hyena was close; his heavy footsteps clumped upon the stones as he hurried near in his dragging, slouching manner. Ah-ha! The little mongoose had again found something to eat. He must hurry up and rob him of it.

Had he brains enough for anything but his loathsome deeds, the hyena would have seen the wary movements of the mongoose and exercised caution. But his greed made him imprudent. He hurried close as Bandy nimbly jumped aside. Open-mouthed, the hyena came to gulp up whatever Bandy was feeding on. His staring eyes were almost upon the viper before his nose told him of his great peril. His forefeet slid on the rocky ground as he tried to apply his brakes and stop his impetuous rush. But it was too late. That ugly horn-studded head whipped forward and caught him right in the open mouth.

"*Ahragh! Whoo-ough-uh — who-ugh — wow-ooo!*" The big brute sprang into the air; he rolled upon the ground. Jerkily, he kicked his feet. He bit at grass, at earth, at stones about him. At last, he quivered and lay still.

Bandy stood up as straight as a reed stands in a marsh. He made no sound as he looked upon this drama. He did not even bother to kill the viper. This could wait until some hungry time. Dropping to his short legs, he set out upon the trail for home. He was mumbling to himself as he looked about before entering his burrow. His mumbling sounded like people in low conversation. Maybe he was telling himself that he had at last evened the score with the bat-eared hyena clan.

11: Striped Strategy

Little Waha galloped over the grass-covered African veld, running hard at his mother's side. Although he was but a week old, Waha could run fast. He had long legs for his size. Nature provides long legs for those who must keep up with a running herd when young. His coat was long and woolly, for the nights on the high veld of East Africa are often cold. His soft colt's hair was striped with light brown. Later, when he grew older and shed this soft coat, he would be sleek like the older zebras. Then he would have dark chocolate-brown stripes, looking black from a little distance.

This evening, the veld was noisy with drumming hoofs and the high-pitched "*qua-ha, qua-ha*" of alarmed zebras. They snorted and squealed as they ran, kicking and biting at others who crowded too closely; raising a cloud of dust that was carried like smoke by the wind.

The deep-throated rumbling roar of a lioness thundered into the gathering shadows of night. One zebra had not run away fast enough and the lioness was sending out the dinner call to the rest of her pride. In the gathering gloom of evening, through the long grass, five lions

came stalking to her call. These were of various ages — the lioness's grown and growing young.

As the lions settled down to their evening meal, the zebras seemed to know that the danger was over and it was again safe to stop and graze. This was the middle of the dry season. The grass was dry and yellow, but the heavy seed-tops kept the zebras fat. Like oats, the grass seeds are fattening, and all the zebras looked round and well fed. As they grazed, they kept alert. While his mother grazed, Waha helped himself to a drink of milk. He was always thirsty. It was so very dry and dusty on the big veld.

Wildebeest, or white-bearded gnus — dark gray antelope, looking somewhat like bison from a distance — switched their long black tails and grunted at the zebras. They banded together with the zebras in a sort of mutual-protection society. Each snorted to warn the other when danger approached. Danger was easier to avoid when so many eyes, ears, and noses were alert. On the African veld, the slogan is not "Stop, look, and listen," it is "Sniff, look, listen, and run."

In the early morning, as the sun rose and the weaver birds began twittering in the thorn trees, the zebras and gnus were at the water hole. Many other animals were there, too. There was a herd of the brown kongoni antelope, with backward-twisted horns set high, on an extension, or pedicel, at the top of the head. Also, there were many little gazelles. These smartly dressed little fellows, with bold, black stripes along their sides, were everlastingly wagging their little tails. Ostriches came strutting along like ballet dancers balancing on their toes. Everyone knew that the ostriches could kick very fast and hard. All made room for the big birds, stepping aside and leaving a lane for them to pass through. It was just like a big circus menagerie. Baboons were here to represent the monkey clan.

Waha still looked with wonder, mixed with a bit of distrust, at all these other animals. When one is just two weeks old there is much at which to look and learn. He was not too sure about the baboons. Everlastingly, these went scampering about everyone's feet, squealing and chasing each other. Waha understood the grass-eating animals best. Different kinds of antelope were various sizes and colors, but they were hoofed and went in herds like the zebras. He trusted these.

Now, some tall animals came to the water hole, towering high over everyone. Waha crowded close to his mother. These, too, were hoofed animals, but they were so very immense beside all the others. He really did not have to worry about them. Giraffes were good friends of the zebras and they had only come to drink. Spreading their long forelegs apart so they could get their heads down to the water, they looked very awkward as they drank.

Soon, one herd after the other drifted away. The water hole was deserted, except for small birds. The larger animals were now scattered about on the open veld.

Waha's mother lay down in the grass and he lay down beside her. Some of the zebra herd just stood asleep on their feet. Tails lazily switched at flies. For a long time, all seemed very peaceful. Then there was an odd, purring sound. The impala antelope were blowing through their nostrils to clear them for better scenting of danger. This "prr-p-rr" sound went rippling through the impala herd. Gnus honked and snorted. Every zebra was alert and calling "Qua-ha, qua-ha!"

In just a moment, the gnus wheeled into a long flank line and were away with flying tails. Off went the impala on the jump, for they are the supreme high jumpers of Africa.

Nervously, Waha stood beside his mother, who was snorting in alarm.

W.J. Wilwerding

Zebra sentinels, who had posted themselves at a distance on each side of the herd, now came snorting to join the others. Just then, a brown company of kongonis raced past. Caught in the panic, an assembled group of zebra mares and their young ran madly after the kongonis. Waha and his mother ran in the midst of this group.

Now, the cause of the alarm was plainly in sight. Already, the "*hoo-hoo!*" of the hunting call rang bell-like over the veld. The wild dogs of the veld were on the hunt! These bat-eared animals, mottled like a calico cat in black, white, and rusty-yellow, with white-plumed tails waving, were jumping up high over the grass-tops for a look around. Now, these most ruthless hunters of the veld came running in an easy, effortless gallop. Some ran ahead to cut off the retreat of the zebra mares and their foals.

In a very short time, the wild dogs had the zebras milling in a circle, while they yapped and snapped at their flanks. There were a dozen or more wild dogs in this pack and they seemed to have perfect command of the situation. Very sure of themselves and of what they were doing, a few ran in close to drive a young zebra foal from the herd. But they had the zebra mothers to contend with. Snorting and squealing, the mothers struck hard at the wild dogs with their forehoofs. Striking like boxers, they sent the first wild dogs rolling on their backs.

Now the wild dogs stood off for a bit, watching the zebras and barking like collies. They did not seem to be disturbed by the first setback. Hunting was their business and they had all day long in which to accomplish their task. They appeared to be having a good time. They looked for an opening, so they could quickly rush into the herd and start a bit of confusion. In this melee, they could quickly separate a bewildered young one from its mother and drive it forth.

One wild dog made a quick dash at Waha, but the old mare quickly struck at his blunt, black muzzle and sent him whimpering away. Now there was cackling among the wild dogs as if they were talking things over. Apparently, they did come to a decision, for one group stayed on one side where Waha's mother stood on defense. The other wild dogs went around to the other side of the zebra herd.

Their strategy appeared to be to attack fiercely on one side and disconcert the zebras, allowing their comrades to run in and cripple a young one or drive it forth. They now put this evil plan into action. Of a sudden, a half-dozen wild dogs ran in boldly to snap and growl at the zebras. They just stopped short of the snorting mares, who beat at their tormentors with stamping forehoofs. While these other wild dogs were distracting Waha's mother, two wild dogs ran in to attack Waha.

Quickly, the old mare struck at one black muzzle. She sent one dog sprawling. The second one she sent spinning with a rib cracked. At the same time, other zebra mares were busily fighting off other wild dogs. Now a few wild dogs lay off at a little distance, panting with cracked ribs. One that had been stunned by a kick in the head lay still.

Barking excitedly, the remaining wild dogs returned to the attack. Separating into two groups again, one group attacked the zebras from one side, while the other attacked on the other side. The wild dogs were getting a bit reckless now. Boldly leaping in to the attack with snapping jaws, they managed to scatter the mares. A wild dog darted in past Waha's mother. Just then she was busy fighting off another wild dog. Before she could turn and strike at this new peril, he had lunged, snarling, at Waha. In another moment, he had driven the little zebra colt from his mother's protecting hoofs. Wildly, Waha ran toward the main zebra herd. The other zebras, attracted by the tumult of the fighting, were coming closer to investigate the cause of the disturbance. Older stallions were in the lead.

Disregarding the attacking wild dogs, Waha's mother galloped after him, bucking and kicking at wild dogs that were close at her heels. Now the whole wild-dog pack deserted the other mares and foals. All joined in the chase of Waha. This is what they had planned from the very beginning — to separate one zebra from the herd. Now they would drive it until it was exhausted. The end would be a foregone conclusion.

Wild dogs were now closing in on Waha. One of these Waha's mother struck to earth with flailing hoofs. But here, in the open, without others to help, it was difficult to defend Waha from so many. It looked like the end of a most valiant fight to save her foal.

But Waha, through some instinct, or perhaps by accident, had run straight toward the advancing zebra herd. The fighting stallions of the herd now caught the rank smell of the wild dogs. Ears back, snorting and squealing, they came to the attack. One wild dog, who was about to sink fangs into Waha's flank, was battered to earth with trampling hoofs. Other wild dogs were now being trampled and kicked. Some were even bitten by the enraged stallions. Wild dogs that escaped the fury of the stallions did so by sheer luck.

Waha never forgot this experience. Zebras, like domestic horses, have wonderful memories. In after years, he was always alert when he caught sight of those bat ears sticking up above the veld grass, or heard the ringing "hoo-hoo" call of the wild-dog pack. He grew up to be a fine, strong zebra. He was full of high courage and became master of his own herd.

In the evening, on the vast stretches of open veld in northern Tanganyika, you might see Waha, as the rays of the setting sun turn his sleek, striped coat to burnished gold. Proudly, he raises his head to call to his herd. Answering calls ripple through the striped ranks, "Qua-ha, qua-ha, qua-ha!" In a long line of striped equine beauty, the zebras are on their way to the water hole for the evening drink. Old mares, with years of experience in the ways of the wild veld country, are in the lead. They scent the wind and scout ahead for any signs of danger. Waha brings up the rear of the herd to see that all is in order ahead. Soon all are lost to view in the evening's deepening shadows. Their calls become faint with the distance, "QUA-HA, Qua-Ha, qua-ha," until only the nearby yapping of jackals is with us in the dusk of advancing night.

12: Old Wildy

Wildy, the bull gnu, was very old now. The once sharp points on his black horns were blunted with time. His teeth were worn. Strength and speed were no longer in his old limbs. Wildy was lonesome, just as, with family and friends gone, humans are lonesome when they grow old. One wondered what memories Wildy retained of his younger days. He was a blue wildebeest, or white-bearded gnu, with a fringe of long white hair on his lower neck and jaw. He was blue-gray, with black brindle lines on his neck and forequarters. His long, horselike tail was black. He was as big as a cow but more slender of leg and built more for running. His horns grew outward and curved somewhat like those of an African buffalo. From a distance, he was sometimes mistaken for a buffalo.

Perhaps Wildy still remembered the proud days when he was the leader of the gnu herd. That was long ago when he was young and swift and strong. Like all wild animals, he knew every rock, tree, and bush in the land that he knew as his home. Nothing could hide in a tree or bush without his knowing it. He looked at things and he saw when they were not as they should be. This is why he was difficult to ambush and why he had lived to be old. One does not live long in the wilds of

W.J.Wilwerding

Africa or in any other wild place on earth, if one is unobserving or stupid.

Wildy had bested all the other gnu bulls in fair fights to become leader of his herd. In the early African dawn, he had always taken his herd to water. During the long, hot days, he had grazed with them on the open veld. In the sizzling midday hours, he had stood with them beneath what shade the few scattered thorn trees provided. In the early evening, with the red sun low, he had again led them to water.

This gnu's life that Wildy led may seem rather uneventful — going to water, eating grass, resting in the shade, and again going to water, day in and day out. But there were those who lived on the broad veld and in the bush country near the water who kept Wildy from being bored with life. In fact, these creatures not only kept the gnus from being bored, they kept them in running exercise. Some of these were leopards, whom Wildy had to cope with when he was a calf. Lions had to be watched when he was mature. These beasts of prey kept him alert and on the jump. You do not get bored when you must watch everlastingly for those who will kill and eat you. Wildy had to be on guard not only for his own life, but for those of the cows, calves, and growing young of the herd.

There were other things, too, that kept Wildy from being bored with the monotony of everyday existence. Water holes dried up in the long dry season. The dried grass became brittle and was trampled by many hoofs. One had to migrate to find water to drink and new pasturage. Mostly, everybody living on the veld thought about this at the same time or were forced by the long drought to migrate at the same time. One herd joined others and these again joined still others, until the whole vast veld was one mass of migrating gnus, zebras, and other hoofed creatures that lived on grass.

The earth was dry and the vast multitude of hoofs stirred it into powder, so the herds traveled under a cloud of dust. Young were born, old ones lay down to die; weak were pulled down by lions, wild dogs, and hyenas. Flocks of vultures circled in the shimmering sky to drop to earth when some creature's bitter time had come. The strong survived and carried on. So it had been with Wildy. He lost older members of his herd and many young, but the herd had somehow kept its strength of numbers. He had made many migrations in his lifetime until a day came when a younger and stronger bull had driven him from the herd.

At first, Wildy had attempted to follow along behind the herd. When he was again driven away, he tried to follow other gnu herds. The leading bulls of these herds also drove him away. Then he had joined a herd of eland antelope. Since there was no competition between the bulls of the eland herd and old Wildy, he had been tolerated. Always living in company, he was unaccustomed to going about alone and he was happy in the company of the eland herd. The eland were handsome beasts, colored somewhat like Jersey cows, with white stripes on their bodies. They were as large as cattle and had stout, upstanding, twisted black horns. With his blue-gray coat, you could notice Wildy from a long way off when he was with the eland herd.

The herds had migrated to a lake where there was water through the days of drought. African tribesmen herded their humped cattle near this lake to be close to water, so the wild herds usually grazed at some distance from it. The eland herd grazed on a high plateau to the west of the lake, the lake being in the valley below, in what is called the Rift Valley. Groves of big umbrella-mimosa trees grew near the lake. The shores were bordered with yellow-barked acacia trees. The high plateau, where the eland grazed, was grown with scattered gall acacias: small, twisted thorn trees. In between the stunted trees, the grass grew knee-high to the animals. The grass-tops were heavy with seeds. Eland, gnus, and zebras grew fat on this fodder.

Wildy now had no worries about food, nor about water. He had the eland for company. He should have been content, but there was one drawback to this companionship. At the first dread whiff on the air that man or beast was out hunting for them, the eland were off in a fast, swinging trot. Should the danger be immediate, they could, despite their size, go away on the jump like so many oversized impala. At times, one would jump clear over another's back and they readily jumped over the bush tops. At such times, Wildy could not keep up with them. He was accustomed to running on the open veld and was no bush jumper.

Frequently, after an alarm, Wildy was left behind. It was sometimes several days before he again made contact with the eland herd. It is miraculous that some wandering lion did not pull him down. No doubt the sagacity that had once made him leader of his herd still stood him in good stead. Once he wandered about alone for some days and then, seeing a herd of the little tommy gazelles, he joined these. His yearning for company was such that he was eager to join any herd of veld animals.

You could see Wildy from afar when he herded with the gazelles. At first, he seemed to be standing there all alone, but a second look showed that he was surrounded by his little friends, who were partially hidden in the yellow grass. He looked big, black, and buffalolike from a distance. His dainty russet-tan friends were scattered all about him, busy with their grazing and everlastingly wagging their tails. He stood there listlessly switching his horselike tail at flies. Peering intently at anything and everything approaching from afar, he was an excellent watchman for the little gazelles. Apparently they knew this and no doubt were happy to have his company. There is great companionship between the hoofed beasts of the African veld, even between those that are large and those that are small. Humans could learn much from them. The gazelles no doubt had a great affection for their big friend.

So Wildy lived his old days, sometimes with the eland, again with zebras, and more and more with the little gazelles. He was getting less spry with each passing month and no doubt would soon have fallen prey to a lion or a wandering pack of wild dogs, had not a white hunter found him out there all alone one day. The hunter had come to Tanganyika from South Africa. That had been many years ago. Now, like old Wildy, he, too, was old. He lived at the edge of an African village in one of their mud and wattle huts. One day he needed some meat and wanted a skin as a rug for his hut. He found the old bull gnu standing there, big and dark and alone. Wildy did not run from the hunter. He just stood there broadside, with his big, long, homely head turned to watch the approaching hunter. Perhaps he had at last grown tired of running away, maybe even a bit tired of life. He just stood there looking at the hunter until the rifle spoke and then Wildy was no more.

I had watched Wildy for a long time, had seen him with the eland herd, with the zebras, and with the little gazelles. One day I missed him. I asked the Africans whether they had seen him and an Iramba tribesman told me what had happened to Wildy. He took me to where Wildy had met his end. The jackals, hyenas, and vultures had been

93

there and all that remained of the old gnu bull was his whitened skull with the two black horns that were blunt at the tips. Sadly I gathered these and carried them away. His horns hang above my writing desk as I write Wildy's story.

Looking up at Wildy's horns, I am again, in memory, on the wide Wairamba Steppe of central Tanganyika. Wildy is standing there big and black against the yellow grass of the dry season. His little gazelle friends are scattered about in the grass. There is much tail switching at the ever-present flies. In those wandering and adventurous days, when I saw Wildy there, that whole African country was ours to roam in, wide, wild, and free. We are only there in memory now, but the hoofed herds still wander there in life. At the approach of evening, when the long hot day is nearing an end, the veld animals go to water. Impala snort and there is the boisterous "*qua-ha*" of the zebras. The gnus are coming along in a long file and they are honking, "*Kwonk-kwonk.*" Wildy's little gazelle friends follow along, all tails busily wagging. I wonder whether they missed him after he was gone and whether the old ones still remember him.

The Author and Artist

WALTER J. WILWERDING began to develop himself as an animal artist immediately after he graduated from high school. He studied art for the next several years, and for twenty years he spent several days of each week at zoos and circuses, painting animals. He frequently went into the dens of lions and tigers (with the trainers) for close-up work on his sketches. With money earned from his illustrations he financed his first jaunt to Africa in 1929. When he returned he wrote and illustrated four stories, and mailed them hopefully to four different magazines. The mail brought back four acceptances. Since then he has painted hundreds of magazine covers, and authored scores of articles and stories—all with animals as his subjects.

Mr. Wilwerding now lives in Minneapolis with his wife, Sylvia.